HOMOTOPY THEORY

HOMOTOPY THEORY

GEORGE W. WHITEHEAD

Compiled by Robert J. Aumann

THE M.I.T. PRESS
Massachusetts Institute of Technology
Cambridge, Massachusetts, and London, England

Library of Congress Catalog Card Number: 66-15792
Printed in the United States of America

Preface

These are the unaltered notes of a graduate course in homotopy theory which was given at M.I.T. in the fall of 1953. They were compiled by Mr. Robert J. Aumann, Teaching Assistant in the Department of Mathematics. A previous edition of the notes, was distributed for a number of years by the Department of Mathematics at M.I.T. About five years ago, in anticipation of a number of books on homotopy theory which were about to appear, it was decided that the notes had served their purpose and their distribution was discontinued. Since some of the envisioned works never materialized, and since there is evidence of a continuing demand for these notes, they are being reissued in the present form, the pressure of other duties having left me with insufficient time to carry out a wholesale revision.

The notes were designed for a second-year graduate course. A knowledge of two fundamental groups, and of algebraic topology as far as singular theory, is assumed. They were not intended to be complete, but were designed to introduce the student to some of the more important concepts of homotopy theory, and at the same time to lead him to the frontier of research. In the intervening years the subject has grown with great rapidity, and they no longer fulfill the second objective. I believe that they still fulfill the first, although by now the subject matter might be more appropriate for the second term of a first-year course.

Cambridge, Massachusetts
August, 1965

GEORGE W. WHITEHEAD

Contents

HOMOTOPY THEORY

1. Homotopy Groups

1.0 Introduction

The problems with which we shall be concerned here are those of the extension and classification of continuous maps. These may be stated as follows.

EXTENSION PROBLEM (E): Given spaces X, Y, a closed subset A of X, and a map $f:A \to Y$, does there exist a map $g:X \to Y$ such that $g|A = f$? If so, then g is called an extension of f.

CLASSIFICATION PROBLEM (C): Given spaces X, Y, a closed subset A of X, and maps f', f'' of X into Y such that $f'|A = f''|A$, does there exist a map $g:I \times X \to Y$ such that $g(0,x) = f'(x)$, $g(1,x) = f''(x)$ for $x \in X$, and $g(t,x) = f'(x) = f''(x)$ for $x \in A$? (I is the unit interval.) If so, then g is called a *homotopy* of f' to f'' relative to A. If A is the null set, then g is simply called a homotopy of f' to f''.

The classification problem is a special case of the extension problem. For let $X^* = I \times X$, $A^* = 0 \times X \cup 1 \times X \cup I \times A$, and define $f:A^* \to Y$ by $f(0,x) = f'(x)$, $f(1,x) = f''(x)$, $f(t,x) = f'(x) = f''(x)$ for $x \in A$. Then an extension of f over X^* is exactly a homotopy of f' to f'' relative to A.

On the other hand, under suitable hypotheses on the spaces involved, if f' and f'' are homotopic maps of A into Y, then f' can be extended over X if f'' can. In fact we have the homotopy extension theorem, which may be stated as follows.

THEOREM 1.0.1. *Let X, Y be spaces, $A \subset X$, $f: X \to Y$, $F: A \times I \to Y$ maps such that $f|A = F|A \times \{0\}$. Then if either of the two sets of conditions stated at the end of the theorem are satisfied, there exists a map $G: X \times I \to Y$ such that $G|A \times I = F$, $G|X \times \{0\} = f$. The possible conditions are*

I. *X separable regular, A closed*
Y an absolute neighborhood retract

or

II. *(X, A) finitely triangulable*
Y arbitrary

PROOF. Part I is standard. See, for instance, Hurewicz and Wallman [B.1, p. 86 (Borsuk's theorem)]. For Part II, we need the fact that a finitely triangulable space is an ANR. See, for instance, Lefschetz [B.2, p. 292].

Let $\tilde{Y} = A \times I \cup X \times \{0\}$, $\tilde{F}$ and $\tilde{f}$ the identity. By the foregoing remark, Y is an ANR. It follows from Part I that there exists a map

$$\tilde{G}: X \times I \to \tilde{Y}$$

such that $\tilde{G}|\tilde{Y}$ is the identity. Then the map $G: X \times I \to Y$ given by

$$G(p) = (f \circ \tilde{G})(p) \qquad \tilde{G}(p) \in X \times \{0\}$$
$$G(p) = (F \circ \tilde{G})(p) \qquad \tilde{G}(p) \in A \times I$$

satisfies the conditions of the theorem.

COROLLARY 1.0.2. *Let $(K; L, K_0)$ be a finitely triangulable triad, $L_0 = K_0 \cap L$. Let*

$$f: (K, L) \to (X, A)$$
$$\phi: (K_0 \times I, L_0 \times I) \to (X, A)$$

be maps with $\phi(x,0) = f(x)$ for $x \in K_0$. Then there is a map $\psi: (K \times I, L \times I) \to (X, A)$ such that

$$\begin{cases} \psi(x,0) = f(x) & (x \in K) \\ \psi(x,t) = \phi(x,t) & (x \in K_0) \end{cases}$$

PROOF. The pair (L, L_0) being triangulable, there is a map $g: L \times I \to A$ such that

$$\begin{cases} g(x,0) = f(x) & (x \in L) \\ g(x,t) = \phi(x,t) & (x \in L_0) \end{cases}$$

Define $h: (K_0 \cup L) \times I \to X$ by

$$h(x,t) = \begin{cases} \phi(x,t) & (x \in K_0) \\ g(x,t) & (x \in L) \end{cases}$$

The pair $(K, K_0 \cup L)$ being triangulable, there is a map $\psi: K \times I \to X$ such that

$$\begin{cases} \psi(x,0) = f(x) & (x \in K) \\ \psi(x,t) = h(x,t) & (x \in K_0 \cup L) \end{cases}$$

Then ψ is the desired map.

We now give examples in which we demonstrate necessary conditions for the solubility of (C) and (E). In general, these conditions will be far from sufficient, as will be demonstrated later.

THEOREM 1.0.3. *Let E be an n-cell, S its boundary, and let $f: S \to Y$. Then a necessary condition that f be extendable to a map $g: E \to Y$ is that the induced homomorphism $f_*: H_{n-1}(S) \to H_{n-1}(Y)$ be identically zero.*

PROOF. Let $i: S \to E$ be the inclusion map. If g exists, then $f = g \circ i$, and hence $f_* = g_* \circ i_*$. But i_* is identically 0, since $H_{n-1}(E) = 0$.
Q.E.D.

REMARK. *It is easy to see that S may be replaced by any subset of E, and $n - 1$ by any integer greater than* 0.

THEOREM 1.0.4. *Under the same conditions as those of Theorem* 1.0.3, *let $f', f'': S \to Y$. Then, in order for f' and f'' to be homotopic, it is necessary that the induced maps f'_* and f''_* on the homology groups be equal.*

PROOF. Since f' and f'' are homotopic, the maps $f'_\#$ and $f''_\#$ induced by f' and f'', respectively, on the singular complex of S are chain-homotopic. But it is well known that chain-homotopic maps on a complex induce the same map on the homology groups. Q.E.D.

REMARK. *The same remark holds for Theorem* 1.0.4 *as for Theorem* 1.0.3.

At present, the foregoing problems have been solved only in a few special cases. If either X or Y is a cell, the problem of classifying the maps of X into Y is trivial. But if X is so simple a space as an n-sphere, the classification problem is far from solved, although great progress has been made in the last few years. The attempt to solve the latter problem ($X = S^n$) led Hurewicz to define the homotopy groups, which may be thought of as higher dimensional generalizations of the fundamental group. In this chapter we describe the basic properties of the homotopy groups; later we shall show how they are used in attacking the general extension and classification problems.

1.1 Function Spaces [7, 16]

Let X and Y be topological spaces.

DEFINITION. $N(A,B) = \{f \mid f: X \to Y, f(A) \subset B\}$ *for* $A \subset X$, $B \subset Y$.

DEFINITION. Y^X = *space of all maps (continuous functions)* $f: X \to Y$, *with the smallest topology containing all sets* $N(C,U)$, C *compact and contained in* X, U *open and contained in* Y. *This is called the compact-open topology.*

LEMMA 1.1.1. *Let* X *be Hausdorff;* O_i *open* $\subset X$, $i = 1, \cdots, n$;

$$C \text{ compact} \subset O = \bigcup_{i=1}^{n} O_i$$

Then $\exists\, C_i$ such that

$$C = \bigcup_{i=1}^{n} C_i$$

$$C_i \text{ closed} \subset O_i$$

$i = 1, \cdots, n$.

PROOF. Standard. See Lefschetz [B.2, p. 26 (33.4)(a)].

LEMMA 1.1.2. *Let* A *be a subbasis for the topology of* Y. *If* X *is Hausdorff, then the sets* $N(C,U)$, C *compact,* $U \in A$, *form a subbasis for the topology of* Y^X.

PROOF. It suffices to show that, for each f and $N(C,U)$, C compact, U open, $f \in N(C,U)$, there exist compact sets C_i and members U_i of A, $i = 1, \cdots, m$, with

$$f \in \bigcap_{i=1}^{m} N(C_i,U_i) \subset N(C,U)$$

Now since A is a subbasis, we certainly have $U = \bigcup_{\alpha} V_\alpha$, where each V_α is a finite intersection of elements of A. Now $f(C) \subset U$, so $C \subset f^{-1}(U) = f^{-1}(\bigcup_{\alpha} V_\alpha) = \bigcup_{\alpha} f^{-1}(V_\alpha)$. Since C is compact, it follows that

$$C \subset \bigcup_{i=1}^{n} f^{-1}(V_{\alpha_i})$$

with the V_{α_i} picked from among the V_α. From Lemma 1.1.1 it follows that there exist closed subsets C_i of C, $i = 1, \cdots, n$, with

$$C_i \subset f^{-1}(V_{\alpha_i}) \qquad \text{and} \qquad C = \bigcup_{i=1}^{n} C_i$$

Let $V_{\alpha_i} = U_{i,1} \cap \cdots \cap U_{i,k_i}, U_{i,j} \in A$. Then

$$f \in \bigcap_{i=1}^{n} \bigcap_{j=1}^{k_i} N(C_i, U_{i,j}) \subset N(C,U)$$

For $f(C_i) \subset V_{\alpha_i} \subset U_{i,j}$, i.e., $f \in N(C_i, U_{i,j})$; and if $g \in N(C_i, U_{i,j})$, then $g(C_i) \subset U_{i,j}$, $g(C_i) \subset \bigcap U_{i,j} = V_{\alpha_i} \subset U$. But the C_i exhaust C; so $g(C) \subset U$, $g \in N(C,U)$. This completes the proof.

Let X, Y, Z be topological spaces. Then, if f takes X into Z^Y, we denote by f^* that function from $X \times Y$ into Z which takes (x,y) into $f(x)(y)$.

THEOREM 1.1.3. *a.* $f^* \in Z^{X \times Y} \Rightarrow f \in (Z^Y)^X$

b. $f \in (Z^Y)^X$, Y locally compact and Hausdorff

$f^* \in Z^{X \times Y}$

PROOF. a. Suppose $f^* \in Z^{X \times Y}$. It suffices to prove that if $x \in X$ and $f(X) \in N(C,U)$, with C compact and U open, then $\exists$ a neighborhood V of X such that $f(V) \subset N(C,U)$. Now if $y \in C$, we have $f^*(x,y) = f(x)(y) \in f(x)(C) \subset U$; hence $\exists$ neighborhoods V_y of x and W_y of y such that $f^*(V_y \times W_y) \subset U$. The sets W_y cover C, and therefore there exist $y_1, \cdots, y_n \in C$ with $C \subset W_{y_1} \cup \cdots \cup W_{y_n}$. Let $V = V_{y_1} \cap \cdots \cap V_{y_n}$. Then if $x' \in V$, $y \in C$, we have, for some i, $y \in W_{y_i}$. Also $x' \in V \subset V_{y_i}$ and therefore

$$f^*(x',y) \in f^*(V_{y_i} \times W_{y_i}) \subset U$$

Thus $f^*(V \times C) \subset U, f(x) \subset N(C,U)$. Q.E.D.

b. Suppose, on the contrary, that $f \in (Z^Y)^X$. Let $x \in X$, $y \in Y$, and let U be a neighborhood of $f^*(x,y)$. Since $f(x) \in Z^Y$ and Y is locally compact Hausdorff, there exists a compact neighborhood W of y such that $f(x)(W) \subset U$; i.e., $f(x) \in N(W,U)$. Since f is continuous and $N(W,U)$ is a neighborhood of $f(x)$, there exists a neighborhood V of x such that $f(V) \subset N(W,U)$. Then $V \times W$ is a neighborhood of (x,y) and $f^*(V \times W) \subset U$. Q.E.D.

THEOREM 1.1.4. *If X and Y are Hausdorff and Y is locally compact, then the correspondence $f \to f^*$ is a homeomorphism of $(Z^Y)^X$ onto $Z^{X \times Y}$.*

PROOF. By Theorem 1.1.3, $f \to f^*$ is a 1:1 correspondence ϕ of $(Z^Y)^X$ onto $Z^{X \times Y}$. Now $f \in N(A, N(B,U))$ if and only if $f^* \in N(A \times B, U)$. Hence ϕ maps subbasic open sets onto open sets and therefore ϕ^{-1} is continuous. Conversely, let $f \in (Z^Y)^X$ and let C be a compact subset of $X \times Y$, U an open subset of Z, such that $f^* \in N(C,U)$. Let A and

B be the projections of C into X and Y, respectively. If $(x,y) \in C$, then there exist neighborhoods $V_{x,y}$ of x relative to A, and $W_{x,y}$ of y relative to B, such that $f^*(V_{x,y} \times W_{x,y}) \subset U$. Now we may assume without loss of generality that $V_{x,y}$ and $W_{x,y}$ are compact; for A and B are compact Hausdorff spaces, and thus are regular. Thus even if $V_{x,y}$ and $W_{x,y}$ are not closed, they contain closed neighborhoods of x and y, respectively; and these will be compact, since closed subsets of compact spaces are compact. Now

$$C \subset \bigcup_{(x,y) \in C} (V_{x,y} \times W_{x,y})$$

Since C is compact, it follows that

$$C \subset \bigcup_{i=1}^{n} [V_{(x_i,y_i)} \times W_{(x_i,y_i)}], \qquad (x_i,y_i) \in C_i, \qquad i = 1, \cdots, n$$

Then if we can show

1. $f \in \bigcap_{i=1}^{n} N(V_{x_i,y_i}, N(W_{x_i,y_i}, U))$

and

2. $g \in \bigcap_{i=1}^{n} N(V_{x_i,y_i}, N(W_{x_i,y_i}, U)) \Rightarrow g^* \in N(C,U)$

then the proof is complete; for then the right side of Part 1 is a neighborhood of f, and by Part 2 is sent into the given neighborhood of $\phi(f)$ by ϕ, and so ϕ is continuous. If the given neighborhood were

$$\bigcap_{i=1}^{m} N(C_i, U_i)$$

then we could have obtained the corresponding neighborhood of f by intersecting the appropriate neighborhoods. Part 1 follows from the fact that

$$f^*(U_{x_i,y_i} \times W_{x_i,y_i}) \subset U, \qquad i = 1, \cdots, n$$

i.e.,

$$f^* \in N(V_{x_i,y_i} \times W_{x_i,y_i}, U), \qquad i = 1, \cdots, n$$

i.e.,

$$f \in N(V_{x_i,y_i}, N(W_{x_i,y_i}, U)) \qquad i = 1, \cdots, n$$

and Part 2 follows from

$$\begin{aligned} & g \in N(V_{x_i,y_i}, N(W_{x_i,y_i}, U)) && i = 1, \cdots, n \\ \Rightarrow\ & g^* \in N(V_{x_i,y_i} \times W_{x_i,y_i}, U) && i = 1, \cdots, n \\ \Rightarrow\ & g^*(V_{x_i,y_i} \times W_{x_i,y_i}) \subset U && i = 1, \cdots, n \\ \Rightarrow\ & g^*(\bigcup_i V_{x_i,y_i} \times W_{x_i,y_i}) \subset U \end{aligned}$$

$\Rightarrow g^*(C) \subset U \Rightarrow g^* \in N(C,U)$. Q.E.D

THEOREM 1.1.5. *$(f,x) \to f(x)$ is a map of $Y^X \times X$ into Y, if X is locally compact Hausdorff.*

PROOF. Let $\phi\colon Y^X \to Y^X$ be the identity map, which is certainly continuous. Then $\phi^*(f,x) = \phi(f)(x) = f(x)$. Q.E.D.

THEOREM 1.1.6. *Suppose B_i are closed subsets of a topological space X,* $i = 1, \cdots, n$, and that

$$\bigcup_{i=1}^{n} B_i = X$$

Suppose further that we are given n continuous mappings $f_i\colon B_i \to Y$, with $f_i|B_i \cap B_j = f_j|B_i \cap B_j$ for all i,j. Then if we define $f\colon X \to Y$ by $f|B_i = f_i$, we have that f is continuous.

PROOF. Standard.

THEOREM 1.1.7. *Let X and Y be spaces, Z a locally compact Hausdorff space, and let $\{A_1,\cdots,A_n\}$ be a closed covering of Z. Let $\theta_i\colon A_i \to X$ be maps. Let*

$$H = \{(f_1,\cdots,f_n) \in Y^X \times \cdots \times Y^X | f_i \circ \theta_i|A_i \cap A_j = f_j \circ \theta_j|A_i \cap A_j \quad i,j = 1, \cdots, n\}$$

Define $\phi\colon H \to Y^Z$ by

$$\phi(f_1,\cdots,f_n)(z) = f_i(\theta_i(z)), \qquad z \in A_i$$

Then ϕ is continuous.

PROOF. By Theorem 1.1.3, it suffices to prove that $\phi^*\colon H \times Z \to Y$ is continuous. For this, it suffices by Theorem 1.1.6 to prove that $\phi^*|H \times A_i$ is continuous. But this is the composite of

$$(f_1,\cdots,f_n,z) \to (f_i,z) \to (f_i,\theta_i(z)) \to f_i(\theta_i(z))$$

The first function is continuous because it is a projection; the second because θ_i is; and the third by Theorem 1.1.5.

PROBLEM 1.

Let X, Y, Z be spaces. Then

1. For each $f \in Z^Y$, $g \to f \circ g$ is a map of Y^X and Z^X.
2. For each $f \in Y^X$, $g \to g \circ f$ is a map of Z^Y into Z^X.
3. If Y is locally compact and Hausdorff, then $(f,g) \to g \circ f$ is a map of $Y^X \times Z^Y$ into Z^X.

1.2 Paths and the Fundamental Group

Let X be a space and let $I = \{t \in R | 0 \leq t \leq 1\}$. A *path* in X is a map $f: I \to X$; f is said to *start* at $f(0)$ and to *end* at $f(1)$. A *loop* in X is a path f such that $f(0) = f(1)$; the loop f is said to be *based at* the point $f(0) = f(1)$ of X.

Let f,g be paths in X such that $f(1) = g(0)$. We define a new path $f \cdot g$ by

$$(f \cdot g)(t) = \begin{cases} f(2t) & (0 \leq t \leq \frac{1}{2}) \\ g(2t - 1) & (\frac{1}{2} \leq t \leq 1) \end{cases}$$

Clearly $f \cdot g$ is a path starting at $f(0)$ and ending at $g(1)$. We also define a path $\hat{f}$ by

$$\hat{f}(t) = f(1 - t) \qquad (t \in I)$$

$\hat{f}$ is a path from $f(1)$ to $f(0)$.

THEOREM 1.2.1.
1. *$(f,g) \to f \cdot g$ is a map of $F = \{(f,g) \in X^I \times X^I | f(1) = g(0)\}$ into X^I.*
2. *$f \to \hat{f}$ is a map of X^I into X^I.*

PROOF. The Proof follows from Theorem 1.1.7, with $Y = X$, $X = I$, $Z = I$.

1. Here we set $A_1 = [0,\frac{1}{2}]$, $A_2 = [\frac{1}{2},1]$, $\theta_1(x) = 2x$, $\theta_2(x) = 2x - 1$.
2. Here we set $A = [0,1]$, $\theta(x) = 1 - x$.

For $x \in X$, let e_x be the constant map of I into the point x; e_x is a path from x to x. If f is a path from x to y, then $\hat{f}$ is a path from y to x. If f is a path from x to y and g a path from y to z, then $f \cdot g$ is a path from x to z. Let $C(X,x)$ be the set of points of X which can be joined to x by a path; $C(X,x)$ is called the *path component* of x in X. The path components form a decomposition of X, in virtue of the foregoing remarks. We say that X is *pathwise-connected* or 0-*connected* if and only if $C(X,x) = X$ for some (and therefore for all) $x \in X$. Define $x \equiv y$ if and only if $\exists$ a path in X from x to y.

We readily verify the following Theorem.

THEOREM 1.2.2.
1. *$C(X \times Y,(x,y)) = C(X,x) \times C(Y,y)$.*
2. *If $f: X \to Y$ is a map, then $f(C(X,x)) \subset C(Y,f(x))$.*

Let $F(X,x,y)$ be the space of all paths in X from x to y. If $f,g \in F(X,x,y)$ then $f \equiv g$ if and only if $g \in C(F(X,x,y),f)$. Thus $f \equiv g$ if and only if $\exists$ a map $h: I \times I \to X$ such that

$$\begin{cases} h(s,0) = f(s) \\ h(s,1) = g(s) \\ h(0,t) = x \\ h(1,t) = y \end{cases}$$

We have the following Corollary to the continuity of multiplication and inversion.

COROLLARY 1.2.3.
1. *If* $f \equiv f'$ *and* $g \equiv g'$, *then* $f \cdot g \equiv f' \cdot g'$.
2. *If* $f \equiv f'$ *then* $\bar{f} \equiv \bar{f}'$.

PROOF.
1. We have $f' \in C(F(X,x,y),f)$
$g' \in C(F(X,y,z),g)$
By Theorem 1.2.2 (1), we have

$$(f',g') \in C(F(X,x,y) \times F(X,y,z),(f,g))$$

Suppose we denote by ψ the map in Theorem 1.2.1 (1). Then $\psi' = \psi|F(X,x,y) \times F(X,y,z)$ is certainly continuous, and we have

$$\psi' : F(X,x,y) \times F(X,y,z) \to F(X,x,z)$$

Thus from Theorem 1.2.2 (2) it follows that

$$\begin{aligned} f' \cdot g' &= \psi(f',g') \\ &= \psi'(f',g') \in \psi'(C(F(X,x,y) \times F(X,y,z),(f,g))) \subset C(F(X,x,z) \end{aligned}$$

$\psi'(f,g)) = C(F(X,x,z),f \cdot g)$. Q.E.D.

2. This follows in a similar manner from Theorem 1.2.1 (2) and Theorem 1.2.2 (2). Theorem 1.2.2 (1) is not used, although Theorem 1.2.2 (2) was needed in the proof of Theorem 1.2.3 (1).

Let $\pi_1(X,x,y)$ be the set of path components of $F(X,x,y)$. We shall abbreviate $F(X,x,x)$ and $\pi_1(X,x,x)$ to $F(X,x)$ and $\pi_1(X,x)$. By the Corollary, we see that the operations on paths induce operations on the equivalence classes: If $\alpha \in \pi_1(X,x,y)$, $\beta \in \pi_1(X,y,z)$, then we may define without ambiguity

$$\alpha \cdot \beta = C(F(X,x,z),f \cdot g)$$

$$\alpha^{-1} = C(F(X,y,x),\bar{f})$$

for any $f \in \alpha$, $g \in \beta$.

To prove that the operations above have reasonable properties, we prove the following Theorem.

THEOREM 1.2.4.

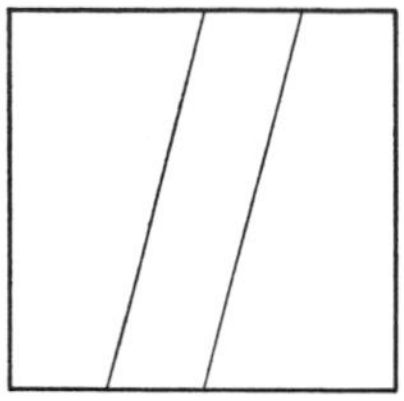

1. $(f,g,h) \to (f\cdot g)\cdot h$ *and* $(f,g,h) \to f\cdot(g\cdot h)$ *are homotopic maps of a subset* G *of* $X^I \times X^I \times X^I$ *into* X^I.
2. $f \to f\cdot e_{f(1)}$ *is homotopic to the identity map of* X^I.
3. $f \to f\cdot f$ *and* $f \to e_{f(0)}$ *are homotopic maps of* X^I *into* X^I.

PROOF.
1. Let $G = \{(f,g,h) | f(1) = g(0) \text{ and } g(1) = h(0)\}$. Define a map $\phi: G \times I \to X^I$ by

$$\phi(f,g,h,t|(s) = \begin{cases} f\left(\dfrac{4s}{1+t}\right) & 0 \leq s \leq \dfrac{1+t}{4} \\ g(4s - t - 1) & \dfrac{1+t}{4} \leq s \leq \dfrac{2+t}{4} \\ h\left(\dfrac{4s-t-2}{2-t}\right) & \dfrac{2+t}{4} \leq s \leq 1 \end{cases}$$

We verify easily that $\phi(f,g,h,0) = (f\cdot g)\cdot h$ and $\phi(f,g,h,1) = f\cdot(g\cdot h)$.

To prove continuity let $\phi_1: G \to (X^I)^I$ be the function defined by ϕ (i.e., $\phi = \phi_1^*$), and let σ be the natural homeomorphism of $(X^I)^I$ onto $X^{I\times I}$. Then it is sufficient to prove $\sigma \circ \phi_1 \cdot G \to X^{I\times I}$ is a mapping.

We now apply Theorem 1.1.7, with $\bar{Y} = X$, $Z = I \times I$, $Y = I$,

$$A_1 = \left\{(s,t) \in I \times I | 0 \leq s \leq \frac{1+t}{4}\right\}$$

$$A_2 = \left\{(s,t) \in I \times I \middle| \frac{1+t}{4} \leq s \leq \frac{2+t}{4}\right\}$$

$$A_3 = \left\{(s,t) \in I \times I \middle| \frac{2+t}{4} \leq s \leq 1\right\}$$

$$\theta_1 = \frac{4s}{1+t}$$

$$\theta_2 = 4s - t - 1$$

$$\theta_3 = \frac{4s-t-2}{2-t}$$

Since it is easily verified that the conditions of Theorem 1.1.7 are satisfied, it follows that $\sigma \circ \phi_1$ is continuous. Thence, since σ is a homeomorphism, it follows that ϕ_1 is continuous, and therefore ϕ. Q.E.D.

2. Define $\psi: X^I \times I \to X^I$ by

$$\psi^*(f,t)(s) = \begin{cases} f\left(\dfrac{2s}{1+t}\right) & 0 \leq s \leq \dfrac{1+t}{2} \\ f(1) & \dfrac{1+t}{2} \leq s \leq 1 \end{cases}$$

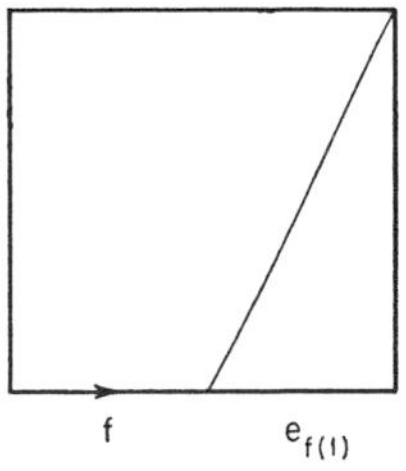

Clearly $\psi(f,0) = f \cdot e_{f(1)}$, $\psi(f,1) = f$. Continuity follows from Theorem 1.1.7 as previously shown.

3. Define $\chi: X^I \times I \to X^I$ by

$$\chi^*(f,t)(s) = \begin{cases} f(0) & 0 \leq s \leq \dfrac{t}{2} \\ f(2s - t) & \dfrac{t}{2} \leq s \leq \dfrac{1}{2} \\ f(2 - 2s - t) & \dfrac{1}{2} \leq s \leq \dfrac{2-t}{2} \\ f(0) & \dfrac{2-t}{2} \leq s \leq 1 \end{cases}$$

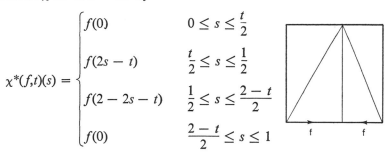

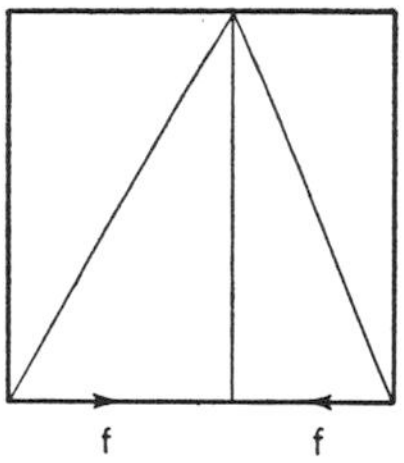

Clearly $\chi(f,0) = f \cdot \hat{f}$, $\chi(f,1) = e_{f(0)}$. Continuity again follows from Theorem 1.1.7.

COROLLARY 1.2.5. *The map $f \to e_{f(0)} \cdot f$ is homotopic to the identity. The maps $f \to \hat{f} \cdot f$ and $f \to e_{f(1)}$ are homotopic.*

PROOF. $e_{f(0)} \cdot f = \widehat{\hat{f} \cdot e_{f(0)}}$ and $\hat{f} \cdot f = \hat{f} \cdot \hat{\hat{f}}$.

COROLLARY 1.2.6. *The operations of multiplication and inversion of homotopy classes have the following properties.*

1. *Each $\alpha \in \pi_1(X,x,y)$ has a left identity ϵ_x and a right identity ϵ_y.*
2. *Each $\alpha \in \pi_1(X,x,y)$ has an inverse α^{-1} with $\alpha\alpha^{-1} = \epsilon_x$, $\alpha^{-1} \cdot \alpha = \epsilon_y$.*
3. *If $\alpha \in \pi_1(X,x,y)$, $\beta \in \pi_1(X,y,z)$, $\gamma \in \pi_1(X,z,w)$, then $(\alpha \cdot \beta) \cdot \gamma = \alpha \cdot (\beta \cdot \gamma)$.*

COROLLARY 1.2.7. *$\pi_1(X,x)$ is a group.*

COROLLARY 1.2.8. *If x and y can be joined by a path in X, then $\pi_1(X,x) \approx \pi_1(X,y)$.*

For let $\alpha \in \pi_1(X,x,y)$. For $\beta \in \pi_1(X,x)$ let $\phi(\beta) = \alpha^{-1}\beta\alpha$; for $\gamma \in \pi_1(X,y)$ let $\psi(\gamma) = \alpha\gamma\alpha^{-1}$. Then ϕ and ψ are homomorphisms inverse to each other.

1.3 Grouplike Spaces

Let X be a space, $e \in X$. We say that (X,e) is an H-space if and only if $\exists$ a map $\mu:(X \times X,(e,e)) \to (X,e)$ such that the maps $x \to \mu(x,e)$ and $x \to \mu(e,x)$ are homotopic relative e to the identity map $(X,e) \to (X,e)$. X is an IH-space if and only if X is an H-space and $\exists$ a map $\nu:(X,e) \to (X,e)$ such that the maps $x \to \mu(x,\nu(x))$ and $x \to \mu(\nu(x),x)$ are homotopic rel e to the constant map of X into e. X is an AIH-space if and only if X is an IH-space and the maps $(x,y,z) \to \mu(x,\mu(y,z))$ and $(x,y,z) \to \mu(\mu(x,y),z)$ are homotopic rel (e,e,e). (Note: We shall usually abbreviate $\mu(x,y)$ to $x \cdot y$, $\nu(x)$ to x^{-1}.)

REMARK 1.3.0. *A topological group is an AIH-space. If X is any space, $x \in X$, then the space $F'(X,x)$ is an AIH-space under $\mu(f \cdot g) = f \cdot g$, $\nu(f) = f$, in the sense of Section 2.*

If X is an H-space, we may use the multiplication in X to define a new multiplication of paths. Let f,g be paths in X, and let $f \# g$ be the path given by

$$(f \# g)(t) = f(t) \cdot g(t)$$

LEMMA 1.3.1. *Let X be an H-space. Then $(f,g) \to f \# g$ is a map of $X^I \times X^I$ into X^I.*

PROOF. It suffices by Theorem 1.1.3 to show that $(f,g,t) \to (f \# g)(t) = f(t) \cdot g(t)$ is continuous. This can be decomposed as follows:

$$(f,g,t) \to (f(t),g(t)) \to f(t) \cdot g(t)$$

The first is continuous because a map into a product space is continuous if and only if each of the projections is continuous; i.e., we must prove

a. $(f,g,t) \to f(t)$ is continuous

b. $(f,g,t) \to g(t)$ is continuous

The function in Part a is the composition of $(f,g,t) \to (f,t) \to f(t)$. The first is continuous because it is a projection; the second by Theorem 1.1.5. Similarly Part b is true. As for the mapping $(f(t),g(t)) \to f(t) \cdot g(t)$, this is continuous by the definition of H-space.

LEMMA 1.3.2. *Suppose X is an H-space, $f \in X^Y$; define map f',f'' by*

$$f'(t) = f(t) \cdot e$$
$$f''(t) = e \cdot f(t)$$

Then $f \to f'$ and $f \to f''$ are maps of X^I into X^I which are homotopic to the identity.

PROOF. Let $\phi: X \times I \to X$ be a map such that

$$\phi(x,0) = x$$
$$\phi(x,1) = x \cdot e$$
$$\phi(e,t) = e$$

To prove $f \to f'$ homotopic to the identity define $\Phi \cdot X^I \times I \to X^I$ by

$$\Phi(f,t)(s) = \phi(f(s),t)$$

Then $\Phi(f,0) = f, \phi(f,1) = f'$. To show Φ continuous it suffices to show $\Phi^*: X^I \times I \times I \to X$ is continuous. This can be broken up into

$$(f,t,s) \to (f(s),t) \to \phi(f(s),t)$$

and both steps are continuous. The proof for $f \to f''$ is similar.

THEOREM 1.3.3. *Let X be an H-space, $F = F(X,e)$. Then the maps*

$$(f \cdot g) \to f \cdot g$$
$$(f,g) \to g \cdot f$$
$$(f,g) \to f \# g$$

are homotopic maps of $F \times F$ into F.

PROOF. Define $\phi: F \times F \times I \to F$ by

$$\phi(f,g,t)(s) = \begin{cases} f(2s(1-t)) \cdot g(2st) & 0 \leq s \leq \frac{1}{2} \\ f(1-2t(1-s)) \cdot g(2(s+t-st)-1) & \frac{1}{2} \leq s \leq 1 \end{cases}$$

There are several verifications which have to be made.

1. Consistency: if $s = \frac{1}{2}$, the first line gives $f(1-t)g(t)$ and the second gives $f(1-t)g(t)$.
2. $\phi(f,g,t) \in F$: $s = 0$ gives $f(0)g(0) = e \cdot e = e$; $s = 1$ gives $f(1)g(1) = e \cdot e = e$.
3. Continuity: routine (by now).

Now note that

$$\phi(f,g,0)(s) = \begin{cases} f(2s) \cdot g(0) = f(2s) \cdot e = f'(2s) & 0 \leq s \leq \frac{1}{2} \\ f(1)g(2s-1) = e \cdot g(2s-1) = g''(2s-1) & \frac{1}{2} \leq s \leq 1 \end{cases}$$

so that $\phi(f,g,0) = f' \cdot g''$. Also

$$\phi(f,g,\tfrac{1}{2})(s) = f(s) \cdot g(s)$$

so that $\phi(f,g,\frac{1}{2}) = f \# g$. Finally

$$\phi(f,g,1)(s) = \begin{cases} f(0)g(2s) = e \cdot g(2s) = g''(2s) & (0 \leq s \leq \frac{1}{2}) \\ f(2s-1)g(1) = f(2s-1) \cdot e = f'(2s-1) & (\frac{1}{2} \leq s \leq 1) \end{cases}$$

so that $\phi(f,g,1) = g''\cdot f'$. Let $\Phi: X^I \times I \to X^I$, $\tilde{\Phi}: X^I \times I \to X^I$ be maps such that

$$\Phi(f,0) = f \qquad \Phi(f,1) = f'$$
$$\tilde{\Phi}(f,0) = f \qquad \tilde{\Phi}(f,1) = f''$$

Then the mapping

$$\psi: F \times F \times I \to F$$

given by

$$\psi(f,g,t) = \Phi(f,t)\cdot\tilde{\Phi}(g,t)$$

provides a homotopy from $(f,g) \to f\cdot g$ to $(f,g) \to f'\cdot g''$. Similarly $(f,g) \to g\cdot f$ and $(f,g) \to g''\cdot f'$ are homotopic. But we have shown that $(f,g) \to f'\cdot g''$ and $(f,g) \to g''\cdot f'$ are both homotopic to $(f,g) \to f \# g$. From this and the transitivity of homotopy the result follows.

COROLLARY 1.3.4. *Let X be an H-space. Then if* $f \in \alpha \in \pi_1(X,e)$ *and* $g \in \beta \in \pi_1(X,e)$, *then* $f \# g \in \alpha\cdot\beta$.

COROLLARY 1.3.5. *Let X be an H-space. Then* $\pi_1(X,e)$ *is abelian.*

THEOREM 1.3.6. *Let X be an AIH-space,* $F = F(X,e)$. *Denote by* $\tilde{f}$ *the member of F given by* $\tilde{f}(t) = (f(t))^{-1}$. *Then F is an AIH-space under* $\mu(f,g) = f \# g$, $\nu(f) = \tilde{f}$, $e = e'_e$, *where* e'_e = *the constant map of I into e.*

PROOF. 1. $\mu: F \times F \to F$ is continuous.
This follows from Lemma 1.3.1.

2. $\mu(e'_e,e'_e) = e'_e$.
For $(e'_e \# e'_e)(t) = e'_e(t)\cdot e'_e(t) = e\cdot e = e = e'_e(t)$. Thus $e'_e \# e'_e = e'_e$.
3. The maps $f \to \mu(e'_e,f)$ and $f \to \mu(f,e'_e)$ are homotopic relative e'_e to the identity map of $F \to F$.
For let $\phi: X \times I \to X$ with

$$\phi(x,0) = e\cdot x$$
$$\phi(x,1) = x$$
$$\phi(e,s) = e$$

The existence of ϕ is assured by the fact that X is an H-space. Now define

$$\Phi: F \times I \to F$$

by

$$\Phi(f,s)(t) = \phi(f(t),s)$$

Φ is certainly a mapping, and we have

$$\begin{aligned}
\Phi(f,0)(t) &= \phi(f(t),0)\\
&= e\cdot f(t)\\
&= e'_e(t)\cdot f(t)\\
&= (e'_e \# f)(t)\\
\Phi(f,1)(t) &= \phi(f(t),1)\\
&= f(t)\\
\Phi(e'_e,s)(t) &= \phi(e'_e(t),s)\\
&= \phi(e,s)\\
&= e\\
&= e'_e(t)
\end{aligned}$$

It follows that

$$\begin{aligned}
\Phi(f,0) &= e'_e \# f\\
\Phi(f,1) &= f\\
\Phi(e'_e,s) &= e'_e
\end{aligned}$$

similarly for $f \to \mu(f,e'_e)$.

4. $\nu: F \to F$ is continuous.

The proof is similar to that of Lemma 1.3.1.

The rest of the conditions may be proved in a manner similar to that of Part 3.

DEFINITION. *Let* (X,e_X), (Y,e_Y) *be H-spaces,* $f:(X,e_X) \to (Y,e_Y)$. *Then* f *is said to be an H-space homomorphism if and only if* $\mu(f(X_1),f(X_2)) = f(\mu(X_1,X_2))$.

THEOREM 1.3.7. *Let* (X,e_X) *be an AIH-space,* $\pi_0(X,e_X)$ *the set of its path components,* $C(x)$ *the path component of* x *in* X. *Then* $\pi_0(X)$ *is a group under the operation* $C(x) + C(y) = C(\mu(x,y))$, *where* $C(x)$ *is the path component of* x.

PROOF. Evident. The identity is $C(e_X)$.

THEOREM 1.3.8. *Let* (X,e_X), (Y,e_Y) *be AIH-spaces,* $f:(X,e_X) \to (Y,e_Y)$ *an H-space homomorphism. For* $x \in X$, *define* $f_*(C(x)) = C(f(x))$. *Then* $f_*: \pi_0(X,e_X) \to \pi_0(Y,e_Y)$ *is a homomorphism.*

PROOF. We first show that f_* is well defined. Let $x' \in C(x)$. Then clearly $f(x') \in C(f(x))$, since f is continuous. So f_* is indeed well defined. To show it is a homomorphism it is only necessary to show

a. $f_*(C(e_X)) = C(e_Y)$

b. $f_*(C(x) + C(x')) = f_*(C(x)) + f_*(C(x'))$

Part a follows from the hypothesis, while Part b may be shown as follows:

$$f_*(C(x) + C(x')) = f_*(C\mu(x,x')) = C(f(\mu(x,x'))) = C(\mu(f(x),f(x')))$$
$$= C(f(x)) + C(f(x')) = f_*(C(x)) + f_*(C(x'))$$

THEOREM 1.3.9. *Let (X,e_X), (Y,e_Y) be AIH-spaces, $f:(X,e_X) \to (Y,e_Y)$. Then according as f is a homeomorphism onto or onto, $f_*:\pi_0(X,e_X) \to \pi_0(Y,e_Y)$ is an isomorphism onto or onto.*

PROOF. If f is a homeomorphism onto it cannot take two path components into one. So f_* must have kernel zero. On the other hand, let f be onto. Then every path component of Y must be represented in $f(X)$, so that f_* is onto. This completes the proof. Note that in order for f_* to be an isomorphism, it is not sufficient that f be 1:1 onto or even a homeomorphism into. Counterexamples are easy to construct.

1.4 Homotopy Groups [14]

Denote by I^n, as usual, the set of real n-tuples all of whose coordinates are in the interval $0 \leq t \leq 1$ for $n > 0$, and $I^0 = \{0\}$. Define

$$\dot{I}^n = \{(t_1,\cdots,t_n) \in I^n | \prod_{j=1}^{n} (t_j(1 - t_j)) = 0\}$$

(i.e., we simply demand that at least one of the coordinates be either one or zero for $n > 0$) and $\dot{I}^0 = \phi$, the null set. The boundary of I^n in Euclidean n-space is $\dot{I}^n$. Clearly $I^n = I^{n-1} \times I$. Furthermore, we have the following Remark.

REMARK 1.4.1. $\dot{I}^n = \dot{I}^{n-1} \times I \cup I^{n-1} \times \dot{I}$.

PROOF. Obvious.

DEFINITION. *Let X be a space, $x \in X$. Then*

1. $F^n(X,x) = \{f \in X^{I^n} | f(\dot{I}^n) = \{x\}\}$, $\quad n > 0$
   $F^0(X,x) = X$
2. $e_x^n =$ *the constant map of I^n into x,* $\quad n > 0$
   $e_x^0 = x$
3. $\pi_n(X,x) =$ *the set of path components of $F^n(X,x)$,* $\quad n \geq 0$.

LEMMA 1.4.2. *If $n \geq 1$, then $F^n(X,x)$ is homeomorphic with*

$$F^1(F^{n-1}(X,x),e_x^{n-1})$$

under a mapping which takes e_x^n onto $e^1_{e_x^{n-1}}$.

PROOF. This is a consequence of the homeomorphism between $X^{I \times I^{n-1}}$ and $(X^{I^{n-1}})^I$. For, if

$$\phi^*: I \times I^{n-1} \to X, \qquad \phi^*(\dot{I}^n) = (x)$$

then from Lemma 1.4.1, we have $\phi^*(\dot{I} \times I^{n-1}) = (x)$, that is,

$$\phi(\dot{I})(I^{n-1}) = (x)$$

that is,

$$\phi(\dot{I}) = e_x^{n-1} \tag{1}$$

On the other hand, again from Lemma 1.4.1, we have

$$\phi^*(I \times \dot{I}^{n-1}) = (x)$$

that is

$$\phi(I)(\dot{I}^{n-1}) = (x)$$

that is

$$\phi(I) \in F^{n-1}(X,x) \tag{2}$$

From Expressions 1 and 2, we obtain that the image of $F^n(X,x)$ is in $F^1(F^{n-1}(X,x),e_x^{n-1})$. Similarly we may prove that the preimage of $F^1(F^{n-1}(X,x),e_x^{n-1})$ is in $F^n(X,x)$. It remains only to prove that e_x^n goes into $e^1_{e_x^{n-1}}$. But this is easy to verify. This completes the proof.

COROLLARY 1.4.3. *For $n \geq 1$, $F^n(X,x)$ is an AIH-space with $\mu(f,g) = f + g$ and $\nu(f) = -f$ given by*

$$(f+g)(t_1,\cdots,t_n) = \begin{cases} f(t_1,\cdots,t_{n-1},2t_n) & t_n \leq \frac{1}{2} \\ g(t_1,\cdots,t_{n-1},2t_n - 1) & t_n \geq \frac{1}{2} \end{cases}$$

$$(-f)(t_1,\cdots,t_n) = f(t_1,\cdots,t_{n-1},1 - t_n)$$

PROOF. By induction on n. For $n = 1$ it is a consequence of Remark 1.3.0. (In fact, it *is* Remark 1.3.0.) For $n > 1$ it follows immediately from the induction hypothesis, Theorem 1.3.6 and Lemma 1.4.2.

COROLLARY 1.4.4. *For $n \geq 1$, the homeomorphism of Lemma 1.4.2 induces a 1:1 correspondence between $\pi_n(X,x)$ and $\pi_1(F^{n-1}(X,x),e_x^{n-1})$.*

DEFINITION. *We make $\pi_n(X,x)$ into a group by demanding that the correspondence of Corollary 1.4.4 be an isomorphism. $\pi_n(X,x)$ is called the nth homotopy group of (X,x).*

THEOREM 1.4.5. *Let*

$$f \in \alpha \in \pi_n(X,x)$$
$$g \in \beta \in \pi_n(X,x)$$

Then $f + g \in \alpha + \beta$. That is, $\pi_n(X,x) = \pi_0(F^n(X,x),e_x^n)$, as groups.

PROOF. Let $f^* \in F^1(F^{n-1}(X,x),e_x^{n-1})$ correspond to f under the homeomorphism of Lemma 1.4.2 and $\alpha^* \in \pi_1(F^{n-1}(X,x),e_x^{n-1})$ to α under the correspondence of Corollary 1.4.4. Then $f^* \in \alpha^*$, $g^* \in \beta^*$. By Corollary 1.3.4, we have $f^* \# g^* \in \alpha^* + \beta^*$. So by the Definition of $\pi_n(X,x)$, we have $f^* \# g^* \in (\alpha + \beta)^*$. Now

$$(f^* \# g^*)(t_1)(t_2,\cdots,t_n) = (f^*(t_1) + g^*(t_1))(t_2,\cdots,t_n)$$

(here the + is in the *AIH*-space $F^{n-1}(X,x)$)

$$= \begin{cases} f^*(t_1)(t_2,\cdots,2t_n) & t_n \leq \frac{1}{2} \\ g^*(t_1)(t_2,\cdots,2t_n - 1) & t \geq \frac{1}{2} \end{cases}$$

$$= \begin{cases} f(t_1,\cdots,2t_n) & t_n \leq \frac{1}{2} \\ g(t_1,\cdots,2t_n - 1) & t_n \geq \frac{1}{2} \end{cases}$$

$$= (f + g)(t_1,\cdots,t_n)$$

(here the + is in the *AIH*-space $F^n(X,x)$)

$$= (f + g)^*(t_1)(t_2,\cdots,t_n)$$

It follows that $f^* \# g^* = (f + g)^*$. Therefore $(f + g)^* \in (\alpha + \beta)^*$. Since * is 1:1, the result follows.

THEOREM 1.4.6. *$\pi_n(X,x)$ is abelian for $n \geq 2$.*

PROOF. Follows from the definition and Theorem 1.3.5. A more direct proof that $\pi_n(X,x)$ is abelian is suggested by the picture:

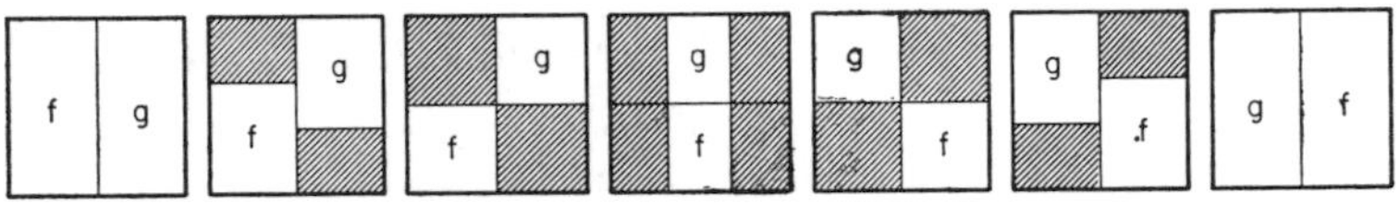

It is left as an exercise to the reader to write down formulas for the homotopies suggested by the picture.

THEOREM 1.4.7. *$F^{n+k}(X,x)$ is homeomorphic with $F^k(F^n(X,x),e_x^n)$ under a homeomorphism which sends e_x^{n+k} into $e^{k}_{e_x^n}$.*

PROOF. For $k = 1$ this is Lemma 1.4.2. The theorem now follows by induction from the fact that the spaces

$$F^k(F^n(X,x),e_x^n)$$

$$F^1(F^{k-1}(F^n(X,x),e_x^n),e_{e_x^n}^{k-1})$$

$$F^1(F^{n+k-1}(X,x),e_x^{n+k-1})$$

$$F^{n+k}(X,x)$$

are homeomorphic, the base points behaving correctly.

LEMMA 1.4.8. *Let $f:(X,x) \to (Y,y)$. Then*

$$\bar{f}:(F^n(X,x),e_x^n) \to (F^n(Y,y),e_y^n)$$

is an H-space homomorphism, where

$$\bar{f}(g)(t_1,\cdots,t_n) = f(g(t_1,\cdots,t_n))$$

PROOF. Continuity follows from Problem 1(1). The homomorphic property is immediate.

COROLLARY 1.4.9. *$\bar{f}_*:\pi_n(X,x) \to \pi_n(Y,y)$ is a homomorphism.*

PROOF. Theorems 1.3.8 and 1.4.5. In the future we shorten $\bar{f}_*$ to f_*.

DEFINITION. *$f \equiv f'$ means f homotopic to f'.*

LEMMA 1.4.10. *Let X, Y be spaces, $f, f':X \to Y, f \equiv f'$. Then $C(f(x)) = C(f'(x))$.*

PROOF. Obvious.

THEOREM 1.4.11. *Let X, Y be spaces, $f, f':(X,x) \to (Y,y), f \equiv f'$ relative x. Then $f_* = f'_*$.*

PROOF. Follows from Problem 1 and Lemma 1.4.8.

THEOREM 1.4.12. *Let X, Y, Z be spaces,*

$$f:(X,x) \to (Y,y), \qquad h:(Y,y) \to (Z,z)$$

Then $(h \circ f)_* = h_* \circ f_*$.

PROOF.
$$\begin{aligned}(h \circ f)_*(C(g)) &= C(h \circ f \circ g)\\ &= h_* C(f \circ g)\\ &= h_* \circ f_*(C(g))\end{aligned}$$

THEOREM 1.4.13. *Let f be the identity map of a space onto itself. Then f_* is the identity.*

PROOF. Utterly trivial. Notice that Theorems 1.4.n, $n = 11,12,13$, show that $\pi_n(X,x)$ satisfy the first two Eilenberg-Steenrod axioms for homology theory, and the fifth.

1.5 The Operations of π_1 on π_n [2, 21]

DEFINITION. $G^n(X) = \bigcup_{x \in X} F^n(X,x)$

$G^n(X)$ *is a subspace* of X^{I^n}

DEFINITION. *The function* π *on* $G^n(X)$ *into* X *is that function for which* $\pi(f) = f(0,\cdots,0)$.

THEOREM 1.5.1. π *is continuous.*

PROOF. $\pi = (g \circ h)|G^n(X)$, where

$$h: X^{I^n} \to X^{I^n} \times I^n$$
$$g: X^{I^n} \times I^n \to X$$

are given by $h(f) = (f,(0,\cdots,0))$
and

$$g(f,t) = f(t)$$

Obviously h is continuous and g is by Theorem 1.1.5.

DEFINITION. *Let* $f,g \in G^n(X)$, $p \in F^1(X,a,b)$. *Then* $f \underset{p}{\equiv} g$ (*f is freely homotopic to g via p*) *if and only if there exists a path q in $G^n(X)$ from f to g such that* $\pi \circ q = p$. *Alternatively*: *There exists a map* $q^*: I^{n+1} \to X$ *such that*

$$q^*(0,t) = f(t),\ q^*(1,t) = g(t), \qquad t \in I^n$$
$$q^*(s,t) = p(s), \qquad t \in \dot{I}^n$$

DEFINITION. *Let* $t \in I^n$. *Then* $|t| = \max_{i=1,\ldots,n} |2t_i - 1|$.

LEMMA 1.5.2. $|t| = 0$ *if and only if* $t = (\frac{1}{2},\frac{1}{2},\cdots,\frac{1}{2})$

$|t| = 1$ *if and only if* $t \in \dot{I}^n$

DEFINITION. *Let* $g \in F^n(X,b)$

$p \in F^1(X,a,b)$

Then $t_p(g)(t_1,\cdots,t_n) = \begin{cases} g(2t_1 - \frac{1}{2},\cdots,2t_n - \frac{1}{2}) & |t| \le \frac{1}{2} \\ p(2 - 2|t|) & |t| \ge \frac{1}{2} \end{cases}$

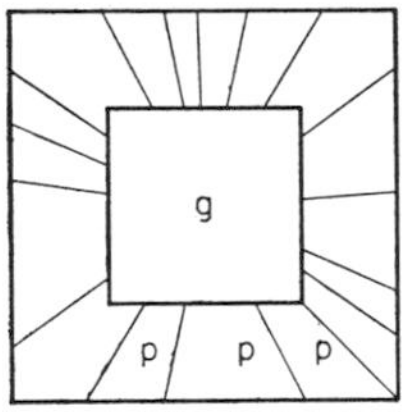

(An idea of what the map looks like is suggested by the accompanying picture.)

LEMMA 1.5.3. $(g,p) \to t_p(g)$ *is continuous from*

$$\bigcup_{a,b \in X} (F^n(X,b) \times F^1(X,a,b)) \text{ to } G^n(X)$$

PROOF. Follows from Theorem 1.1.7. Here $Y = X$, $X = Z = I^n$. $A_1 = \{t \in I^n \big| |t| \leq \frac{1}{2}\}$, $\{A_2 = t \in I^n \big| |t| \geq \frac{1}{2}\}$

$$\theta_1(t_1,\cdots,t_n) = (2t_1 - 1,\cdots,2t_n - 1)$$
$$\theta_2(t_1,\cdots,t_n) = (t_1,\cdots,t_n)$$

It follows that $(g,\tilde{p}) \to t_p(g)$ is continuous, where $\tilde{p}(t_1,\cdots,t_n) = p(2 - 2|t|)$. It remains to prove that $p \to \tilde{p}$ is continuous from X^I to X^{I^n}. This follows from Problem 1, Part 2, once it is shown that $(t_1,\cdots,t_n) \to 2 - 2|t|$ is continuous, which follows from the continuity of $(t_1,\cdots,t_n) \to |t|$. Q.E.D.

THEOREM 1.5.4. *If* $g \equiv g'$ *in* $F^n(X,b)$ *and* $p \equiv p'$ in $F^1(X,a,b)$, then $t_p(g) \equiv t_{p'}(g')$ *in* $F^n(X,a)$.

PROOF. Trivial; merely rewrite the homotopies.

LEMMA 1.5.5. $f \underset{p}{\equiv} g$ *and* $g \underset{q}{\equiv} h \Rightarrow f \underset{pq}{\equiv} h$

LEMMA 1.5.6. $f \underset{p}{\equiv} g \Rightarrow g \underset{\hat{p}}{\equiv} f$

LEMMA 1.5.7. $f \underset{p}{\equiv} f'$, $p \equiv p'$ *in* $F^1(X,f(\dot{I}^n),f'(\dot{I}^n))$

$$\Rightarrow f \underset{p'}{\equiv} f'$$

PROOF. Define a mapping

$$h_r : I^n \to I^n \qquad r \geq \tfrac{1}{2}$$

by $h_r(t_1,\cdots,t_n) = \begin{cases} (\bar{h}(t_1),\cdots,\bar{h}(t_n)), & |t| \leq r \\ (\bar{\bar{h}}(t_1),\cdots,\bar{\bar{h}}(t_n)), & |t| \geq r \end{cases}$

where

$$\bar{h}(t_i) = \frac{2(t_i + r) - 1}{4r}$$

$$\bar{\bar{h}}(t_i) = \frac{t_i}{2(1 - r)} \qquad t_i \leq \frac{1 - r}{2}$$

$$\bar{\bar{h}}(t_i) = \frac{t_i + 1 - 2r}{2(1 - r)} \qquad t_i \geq \frac{1 + r}{2}$$

Obviously h_r is continuous for each r in the range indicated; $h_{1/2}$ is the identity.

Define $t_p^r(g) = t_p(g) \circ h_r$. Then $t_p^{1/2}(g) = t_p(g)$, $t_p^1(g) = g$, and it may easily be shown that the mapping $(r,g,p) \to t_p^r(g)$ is continuous. Let q

be a path from f to f' such that $\pi \circ q = p$, and let k be a path from p to p' in $F^1(X,f(\dot{I}^n),f'(\dot{I}^n))$, $k_s(t) = k(t)(s)$. Now let q' be the path from f to f' given by $q'(s) = t_{k_s}^{|s-\frac{1}{2}|+\frac{1}{2}}(q(s))$. It is easy to show that q' is indeed continuous and satisfies the initial conditions, and thus the result is proved.

LEMMA 1.5.8. *$f \underset{p}{\equiv} g, f' \underset{p}{\equiv} g \Rightarrow f \equiv f'$ in $F^n(X,f(0,\cdots,0))$.*

PROOF. By Lemma 1.5.6, $g \underset{\hat{p}}{\equiv} f'$. By Lemma 1.5.5, $f \underset{p\hat{p}}{\equiv} f'$. But $p\hat{p} \equiv e_{p(0)}$. [For suppose that we consider the composition G of the string of mappings

$$I \times I \to (X^I \times I) \times I \to X^I \times I \to X$$

where the first is the mapping $h(s,t) = ((p,s),t)$, the second is induced by the mapping of Theorem 1.2.5 (3), and the third is that of Theorem 1.1.5. Then G provides a homotopy from $p\hat{p}$ to $e_{p(0)}$.] The result now follows from Lemma 1.5.7 and the trivial fact that $f \equiv f'$ and $f_{ef(0,\cdots,0)} \equiv f'$ are the same statement.

LEMMA 1.5.9. *$t_p(g) \underset{p}{\equiv} g$.*

PROOF. Let $p_s(t) = p(s + t - st)$. Then the path $q(s) = t_{p_s}^{(s+1)/2}(g)$ defines the desired homotopy.

COROLLARY 1.5.10. *$f \underset{p}{\equiv} g$ if and only if $f \equiv t_p(g)$ in $F^n(X,f(\dot{I}^n))$.*

LEMMA 1.5.11. *$f \underset{p}{\equiv} g, f' \underset{p}{\equiv} g' \Rightarrow f + f' \underset{p}{\equiv} g + g'$.*

PROOF. Let ϕ and ϕ' be paths in $G^n(X)$ between f and g and f' and g', respectively, $\pi \circ \phi = \pi \circ \phi' = p$. Then define a path ψ between $f + f'$ and $g + g'$ by $\psi(t) = \phi(t) + \phi'(t)$.

COROLLARY 1.5.12. *$t_p(g + g') \equiv t_p(g) + t_p(g')$ in $F^n(X,p(0))$.*

PROOF. $t_p(g + g') \underset{p}{\equiv} g + g'$. But $t_p(g) \underset{p}{\equiv} g$, $t_p(g') \underset{p}{\equiv} g'$. So $t_p(g) + t_p(g') \underset{p}{\equiv} g + g'$. So $t_p(g + g') \underset{p}{\equiv} t_p(g) + t_p(g')$.

LEMMA 1.5.13. *$t_{e_b}(g) \equiv g$ in $F^n(X,b)$.*

LEMMA 1.5.14. *$t_{pq}(h) \equiv t_p(t_q(h))$.*

PROOF.

$$t_{pq}(h) \underset{pq}{\equiv} h \tag{2}$$

$$t_q(h) \underset{q}{\equiv} h \tag{3}$$

$$t_p(t_q(h)) \underset{p}{\equiv} t_q(h) \tag{4}$$

from Formulas 3 and 4 and Lemma 1.5.5, we have

$$t_p(t_q(h)) \underset{pq}{\equiv} h \tag{5}$$

From Formulas 2 and 5 and Lemma 1.5.7, the result follows.

Let $g \in \alpha \in \pi_n(X,b)$, $p \in \xi \in \pi_1(X,a,b)$. Then $t_p(g)$ is in $F^n(X,a)$; but by Lemma 1.5.4, its path component in $F^n(X,a)$ depends only on the component of g in $F^n(X,b)$, and that of p in $F^1(X,a,b)$, i.e., on α and ξ. So we may state the following Definition.

DEFINITION. *Let $p \in \xi \in \pi_1(X,a,b)$, $g \in \alpha \in \pi_n(X,b)$. Then $\theta_\xi(\alpha)$ is the component of $t_p(g)$ in $\pi_n(X,a)$.*

LEMMA 1.5.15. $\theta_\xi(\alpha + \beta) = \theta_\xi(\alpha) + \theta_\xi(\beta)$

$$\theta_{\epsilon_b}(\alpha) = \alpha \qquad \epsilon_b = C(e_b)$$

$$\theta_{\xi\eta}(\alpha) = \theta_\xi(\theta_\eta(\alpha))$$

PROOF. Lemmas 1.5.n, $n = 12, 13, 14$.

COROLLARY 1.5.16. *θ_ξ is a homomorphism from $\pi_n(X,b)$ to $\pi_n(X,a)$.*

DEFINITION. *Let X be a 0-connected space. A bundle* **G** *of groups in X consists of the following:*

1. *A function which assigns to each $x \subset X$ a group G_x.*
2. *A function which assigns to each $\xi \in \pi_1(X,x,y)$ a homomorphism $\gamma_\xi : G_y \to G_x$, satisfying the following requirements.*
3. *If $\xi \in \pi_1(X,x,y)$, $\eta \in \pi_1(X,y,z)$, then $\gamma_{\xi\eta} = \gamma_\xi \circ \gamma_\eta$.*
4. *If $x \in X$, then $\gamma_{e_x} =$ identity.*

It follows that each γ_ξ is an isomorphism onto, and that the groups G_x are all isomorphic. We frequently write **G** $= \{G_x,\gamma_\xi\}$. *The bundle* **G** *is said to be* simple *if and only if for every $x,y \in X$, ξ, $\eta \in \pi_1(X,x,y)$, we have $\gamma_\xi = \gamma_\eta$.*

THEOREM 1.5.17. *If X is 0-connected, then the system*

$$\pi_n(X) = \{\pi_n(X,x),\theta_\xi\}$$

is a bundle of groups in X.

PROOF. 2, Corollary 1.5.16; 3 and 4, Lemma 1.5.15.

DEFINITION. *The 0-connected space X is said to be n-simple if and only if the bundle $\pi_n(X)$ is simple.*

DEFINITION. *Let $f: Y \to X$ be a map, and let* $\mathbf{G} = \{G_x, \gamma_\xi\}$ *be a bundle of groups in X. We define a new bundle* $f^*\mathbf{G} = \{H_y, \delta_\eta\}$ *by*

$$\begin{cases} H_y = G_{f(y)} \\ \delta_\eta = \gamma_{f*(\eta)} \end{cases}$$

Let $\mathbf{G} = \{G_x, \gamma_\xi\}$, $\mathbf{H} = \{H_x, \delta_\xi\}$ *be bundles of groups in X. A homomorphism* $\phi: \mathbf{G} \to \mathbf{H}$ *is a function which assigns to each $x \in X$ a homomorphism $\phi_x: G_x \to H_x$ satisfying the commutativity relation* $\delta_\xi \circ \phi_y = \phi_x \circ \gamma_\xi$ *for all* $\xi \in \pi_1(X,x,y)$

$$\begin{array}{ccc} G_y & \xrightarrow{\phi_y} & H_y \\ \downarrow{\scriptstyle \gamma_\xi} & & \downarrow{\scriptstyle \delta_\xi} \\ G_x & \xrightarrow{\phi_x} & H_x \end{array}$$

If, for each x,

$$\phi_x \text{ is } \begin{cases} \text{an isomorphism into} \\ \text{onto} \end{cases}$$

we say that

$$\phi \text{ is } \begin{cases} \text{an isomorphism into} \\ \text{onto} \end{cases}$$

If, for each x, $G_x \subset H_x$, *and ϕ_x is the inclusion map, we say that* **G** *is a* subbundle *of* **H**. *If each G_x is a normal subgroup of H_x, we say that* **G** *is a* normal subbundle *of* **H** *and define the* factor bundle **G**/**H** *with groups G_x/H_x and homomorphisms γ_ξ^* induced by γ_ξ.*

DEFINITION. $\Omega_n(X,x_0)$ *is the subgroup of* $\pi_n(X,x_0)$ *generated by all elements of the form* $\alpha - \theta_\xi(\alpha)$ *with* $\alpha \in \pi_n(X,x_0)$, $\xi \in \pi_1(X,x_0)$.

THEOREM 1.5.18. *If* $\xi \in \pi_1(X,x,y)$, *then* $\theta_\xi(\Omega_n(X,y)) \subset \Omega_n(X,x)$. *The system* $\{\Omega_n(X,x), \theta_\xi | \Omega_n(X,y)\} = \Omega_n(X)$ *is a normal subbundle of* $\pi_n(X)$. *The bundle* $\pi_n(X)/\Omega_n(X)$, *denoted by* $\pi_n^*(X)$, *is simple.*

PROOF. We first prove the following Lemma.

LEMMA 1.5.19. $\Omega_n(X,x)$ *is a normal subgroup of* $\pi_n(X,x)$. *In particular,* $\Omega_1(X,x)$ *is the commutator subgroup of* $\pi_1(X,x)$.

PROOF. Since $\pi_n(X,x)$ is abelian for $n > 1$, we may confine our attention to the second statement. By returning to the definition of $t_p(g)$, we see at once that it is homotopic to $(p \cdot g) \cdot \bar{p}$. It follows that $\theta_\xi(\alpha) = \xi\alpha\xi^{-1}$. But $\Omega_1(X,x)$ is generated by the $\alpha\theta_\xi(\alpha)^{-1} = \alpha\xi^{-1}\alpha^{-1}\xi =$

$\alpha\xi^{-1}\alpha^{-1}(\xi^{-1})^{-1}$, and these are precisely the generators of the commutator subgroup. Q.E.D.

Now let $\eta \in \pi_1(X,y)$, $\alpha \in \pi_n(X,y)$. Then

$$\theta_\xi(\alpha - \theta_\eta(\alpha)) = \theta_\xi(\alpha) - \theta_{\xi\eta}(\alpha) = \theta_\xi(\alpha) - \theta_{\xi\eta\xi^{-1}}(\theta_\xi(\alpha))$$

Since $\xi_\eta\xi^{-1} \in \pi_1(X,x)$, the element just described belongs to $\Omega_n(X,x)$. Hence $\theta_\xi(\Omega_n(X,y)) \subset \Omega_n(X,x)$. To prove simplicity of the factor bundle, it suffices to show $\xi,\eta \in \pi_1(X,x,y)$, $\alpha \in \pi_n(X,y) \Rightarrow \theta_\xi(\alpha) - \theta_\eta(\alpha) \in \Omega_n(X,x)$. But

$$\theta_\xi(\alpha) - \theta_\eta(\alpha) = \theta_\xi(\alpha) - \theta_{\eta\xi^{-1}}(\theta_\xi(\alpha))$$

and this element is in $\Omega_n(X,x)$ since $\eta\xi^{-1} \in \pi_1(X,x)$.

We now show that the notion of "bundle of groups" is equivalent to the simpler notion "group with operators in $\pi_1(X)$." In fact, if $\mathbf{G} = \{G_x,\gamma_\xi\}$ is a bundle of groups in X, and $x_0 \in X$, then the homomorphism $\xi \to \gamma_\xi$, ($\xi \in \pi_1(X,x_0)$), defines $\pi_1(X,x_0)$ as group of operators on $G = G_{x_0}$. Conversely, if G is a group on which $\pi_1(X,x_0)$ operates, we define a bundle $\mathbf{G}$ as follows. For each $x \in X$, choose $\xi_x \in \pi_1(X,x_0,x)$ with $\xi_{x_0} = \epsilon_{x_0}$. Then let

$$\bar{G}_x = G$$
$$\bar{\gamma}_\xi(g) = (\xi_x\xi\xi_y^{-1})\cdot g$$

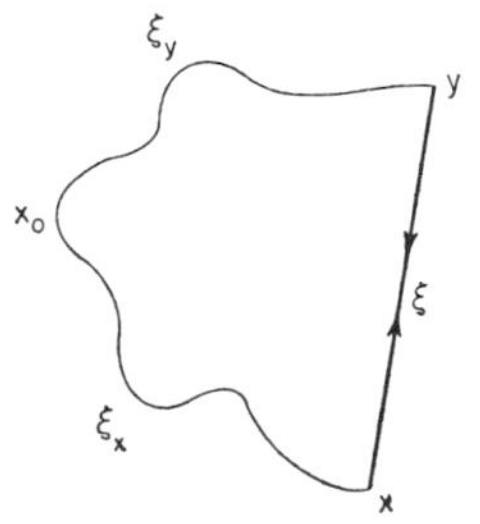

Then $\bar{\mathbf{G}} = \{\bar{G}_x,\bar{\gamma}_\xi\}$ is a bundle of groups in X. If the group G with operators in $\pi_1(X,x_0)$ is derived from a bundle $\mathbf{G}$, then $\mathbf{G} \approx \bar{\mathbf{G}}$ under the isomorphisms $\xi_x\colon G_x \to G_{x_0} = G$. Conversely, the group with operators derived from $\bar{\mathbf{G}}$ is G; for if $\xi \in \pi_1(X,x_0)$, then

$$\bar{\gamma}_\xi(g) = (\xi_x\xi\xi_x^{-1})\cdot g = \xi\cdot g$$

Thus the foregoing correspondence between bundles and groups with operators in π_1 is 1:1.

The notion of bundle of groups is useful in homology theory, as we shall see later. It is actually a special case of Cartan's notion of "faisceau."

REMARK 1.5.20. *Let $f\colon Y \to X$. Then f_* maps $\pi_n(Y)$ homomorphically into $f^*\pi_n(X)$. That is to say: For $\xi \in \pi_1(Y,x,y)$, $\alpha \in \pi_n(Y,y)$, we have* $f_*(\theta_\xi(\alpha)) = \theta_{f_*(\xi)}(f_*(\alpha))$.

1.6 Relative Homotopy Groups [12]

DEFINITION. $J^{n-1} = I \times \dot{I}^{n-1} \cup 0 \times I^{n-1}$. *Let* $x \in A \subset X$. *Then* $F^n(X,A,x)$ = *space of all maps of* $(I^n,\dot{I}^n,J^{n-1}) \to (X,A,x)$, *i.e., those maps of* I^n *into* X *which take* $\dot{I}^n$ *into* A *and* J^{n-1} *into* x.

$\pi_n(X,A,x)$ = *set of path components of* $F^n(X,A,x)$.

LEMMA 1.6.1. $F^n(X,A,x)$ *is homeomorphic with* $F^1(F^{n-1}(X,A,x),e_x^{n-1})$.

PROOF. Similar to that of Lemma 1.4.2.

COROLLARY 1.6.2. *If* $n \geq 2$, $F^n(X,A,x)$ *is an AIH-space with addition the same as for* $F^n(X,x)$.

PROOF. The proof is similar to that of Corollary 1.4.3, insofar as the induction goes. It remains only to establish the truth of the theorem for $n = 2$, and this may be done in standard fashion.

However, it is instructive to pause at this point and examine why the theorem succeeds in this case, whereas it fails for $n = 1$. To this end, we must examine what members of $F^n(X,A,x)$ really are. They are simply maps of I^n into X, in which all faces but one, namely the face $I^{n-1} \times \{1\}$, go into x; while $I^{n-1} \times \{1\}$ goes into A. We denote by J^{n-1} the remainder of the faces, namely the set $\overline{I^n - I^{n-1} \times \{1\}}$. Now when $n > 1$, the sets J^{n-1} and $I^{n-1} \times \{1\}$ intersect, and their intersection is precisely the boundary of $I^{n-1} \times \{1\}$. (We know that they must intersect, because of the connectedness of $\dot{I}^n$ for $n > 1$.) But in the case of $n = 1$, $\dot{I}^{n-1} \times \{1\} = \{1\}$ and $J^{n-1} = \{0\}$ do not intersect. This is made possible by the disconnectedness of $\dot{I}^1$. Now when we add two maps of I^n, we are essentially "gluing" them along the hyperplane $x_n = 1$ of the first map, and $x_n = 0$ of the second. When $n > 1$, this is all right, because these hyperplanes are in J^{n-1}. But when $n = 1$, there are not enough dimensions to force the point 1 to be in J^{n-1}, and so it does not have to go into x, but may go into any point of A. Obviously no gluing can be accomplished if the two parts to be attached are not even brought together.

COROLLARY 1.6.3. $\pi_n(X,A,x)$ *is a group for* $n \geq 2$.

PROOF. Similar to that of Corollary 1.4.4.

COROLLARY 1.6.4. $\pi_n(X,A,x)$ *is abelian for* $n \geq 3$.

PROOF. By definition,

$$\pi_n(X,A,x) \approx \pi_1(F^{n-1}(X,A,x),e_x^{n-1})$$

$F^{n-1}(X,A,x)$ is an H space when $n - 1 \geq 2$, i.e., when $n \geq 3$. Now use Theorem 1.3.5.

COROLLARY 1.6.5. $\pi_n(X,A,x) = \pi_0(F^n(X,A,x),e_x^n)$, *as groups.*

PROOF. Similar to that of Theorem 1.4.5.

COROLLARY 1.6.6. $F^{n+k}(X,A,x)$ *is homeomorphic with*

$$F^n(F^k(X,x),F^k(A,x),e_x^k)$$

under a homeomorphism which is an H-space homomorphism.

PROOF. Similar to that of Lemma 1.4.2, using the natural homeomorphism between $X^{I^{n+k}}$ and $(X^{I^k})^{I^n}$. The fact that the resulting homeomorphism is an H-space homomorphism may be verified by simply examining the additions in the two spaces.

COROLLARY 1.6.7. $\pi_{k+n}(X,A,x) \approx \pi_n(F^k(X,x),F^k(A,x),e_x^k)$.

PROOF. Corollary 1.6.5, Theorem 1.3.9, and, of course, Corollary 1.6.6.

LEMMA 1.6.8. $A = \{x\} \Rightarrow \pi_n(X,A,x) = \pi_n(X,x)$.

DEFINITION. *Let* $n > 1$. *Then the boundary function* $\bar{\partial}$ *from* $F^n(X,A,x)$ *to* $F^{n-1}(A,x)$ *is given by* $(\bar{\partial}f)(t_1,\cdots,t_n) = f(1,t_2,\cdots,t_n)$.

LEMMA 1.6.9. ∂ *is an H-space homomorphism*; (*it is therefore called the boundary mapping*). *Furthermore, if* $\partial_* = \bar{\partial}_*, f:(X,A,x) \to (Y,B,y)$, *then* $\partial_* f_* = (f|A)_*\partial_*$, *and thus the third Eilenberg-Steenrod axiom for homology theory is satisfied by homotopy groups.*

PROOF. We must first check that ∂ is continuous. To this end, consider the mapping $d: X^{I^n} \to X^{I^{n-1}}$, which is induced by the projection $p: I^n \to I^{n-1}$ given by $p(t_1,\cdots,t_n) = p(1,t_2,\cdots,t_n)$. Then the continuity of d follows from that of p by Problem 1, Part 2. But $\bar{\partial} = d|F^n(X,A,x)$. The homomorphism property is readily verified. Commutativity follows from $\bar{\partial}(f \circ g)(t_1,\cdots,t_n) = (f \circ g)(1,t_2,\cdots,t_n) = f(g(1,t_2,\cdots,t_n)) = f((\bar{\partial}g)(t_1,\cdots,t_n))$, where $g \in F^n(X,A,x)$.

From now on through the end of Section 1.6, and occasionally thereafter, we abbreviate our symbols for homotopy groups and H-spaces by omitting explicit mention of the base point x. The resulting symbols are not to be confused with those for the corresponding bundles.

LEMMA 1.6.10. *Let $i\colon A \to X$ and $j\colon (X,x) \to (X,A)$ be inclusion maps, and write $X^k = F^k(X)$, $A^k = F^k(A)$. Then the diagram*

$$\begin{array}{ccccccccc}
\pi_{n+1}(A^k) & \xrightarrow{i_*} & \pi_{n+1}(X^k) & \xrightarrow{j_*} & \pi_{n+1}(X^k,A^k) & \xrightarrow{\partial_*} & \pi_n(A^k) & \xrightarrow{i_*} & \pi_n(X^k) \\
\downarrow & & \downarrow & & \downarrow & & \downarrow & & \downarrow \\
\pi_{n+k+1}(A) & \xrightarrow{i_*} & \pi_{n+k+1}(X) & \xrightarrow{j_*} & \pi_{n+k+1}(X,A) & \xrightarrow{\partial_*} & \pi_{n+k}(A) & \xrightarrow{i_*} & \pi_{n+k}(X)
\end{array}$$

is commutative, where the vertical homomorphisms are the isomorphisms onto of Corollary 1.6.7. *The lemma holds even when $n = 0$, i_*, j_*,* and ∂_* *being defined in the obvious fashion.*

PROOF. Immediate, upon examination of the homomorphisms involved and the mappings which induce them.

LEMMA 1.6.11. *Suppose that the diagram*

$$\begin{array}{ccccccccc}
\cdots & \longrightarrow & A_1 & \xrightarrow{f_1} & A_2 & \xrightarrow{f_2} & A_3 & \longrightarrow & \cdots \\
 & & \downarrow{\scriptstyle f_6} & & \downarrow{\scriptstyle f_3} & & \downarrow{\scriptstyle f_7} & & \\
\cdots & \longrightarrow & B_1 & \xrightarrow{f_4} & B_2 & \xrightarrow{f_5} & B_3 & \longrightarrow & \cdots
\end{array}$$

is commutative and that the vertical functions are one-one onto. Then if the top sequence is exact, so is the bottom sequence.

PROOF. Before we begin the proof, we ask the reader to recall that by commutativity we mean $f_3 \circ f_1 = f_4 \circ f_6$, $f_7 \circ f_2 = f_5 \circ f_3$, etc. We also note that the sets A_i and B_i in question by no means have to be groups, or even to possess any structure whatsoever, except that they have to have a distinguished zero element, such that all the functions take the zero of one group into the zero of the next. The definition of exactness remains unchanged,

The proof is as follows. We have

$$\begin{array}{lll}
\text{Kernel } f_5 & = f_3 \text{ Kernel } f_5 \circ f_3 & \text{(because } f_3 \text{ is onto)} \\
 & = f_3 \text{ Kernel } f_7 \circ f_2 & \text{(by commutativity)} \\
 & = f_3 \text{ Kernel } f_2 & \text{(because since } f_7 \text{ is 1-1, the only element} \\
 & & \quad \text{which goes into 0 is 0)} \\
 & = f_3 \text{ Image } f_1 & \text{(by exactness)} \\
 & = \text{Image } f_3 \circ f_1 & \\
 & = \text{Image } f_4 \circ f_6 & \text{(by commutativity)} \\
 & = f_4 \text{ Image } f_6 & \\
 & = f_4\,(B_1) & \text{(because } f_6 \text{ is onto)} \\
 & = \text{Image } f_4 &
\end{array}$$

This completes the proof.

LEMMA 1.6.12. *The sequence*

$$\pi_1(A) \xrightarrow{i_*} \pi_1(X) \xrightarrow{j_*} \pi_1(X,A) \xrightarrow{\partial_*} \pi_0(A) \xrightarrow{i_*} \pi_0(X)$$

is internally exact.

PROOF.

ⓐ Kernel $j_* =$ Image i_*

For,

$$\text{Kernel } j_* = \{C(f) \in \pi_1(X) | j_*C(f) = C(e_x)\}$$
$$= \{C(f) \in \pi_1(X) | C(jf) = C(e_x)\}$$

[the components on the left side being taken in the space $F'(X,A)$] $= \{C(f) \in \pi_1(X) | C(f) = C(e_x)\} = \{C(f) \in \pi_1(X) | \exists\ F: I \times I \to X$ such that $F(t,1) = x$, $F(t,0) = f(t)$, $F(0,t) = x$, $F(1,t) \in A\}$ [the latter conditions because the homotopy must take place in $F^1(X,A)$]. Now let $g(t) = F(1,1-t)$. Then $g(t) \in A$, $g(1) = F(1,0) = f(0) = x$, $g(0) = F(1,1) = x$. Define

$$G(t,s) = \begin{cases} F(t,2s(1-t) & s \leq \frac{1}{2} \\ F(1-2(1-s)(1-t),1-t) & s \geq \frac{1}{2} \end{cases}$$

Then $G(t,s)$ provides a homotopy in X between $g(t)$ and $f(t)$, so $C(f) = C(g)$ in X. But $g \in F^1(A)$, so

$$C(f) = C(g) = C(ig) \text{ in } X$$
$$= i_*C(g) \text{ in } A$$

So $C(f) \in$ Image i_*. It follows that Kernel $j_* \subset$ Image i_*. The opposite inequality is proved in a similar fashion.

ⓑ Kernel $\partial_* =$ Image j_*

For the image of j_* consists of the set of path components of $F^1(X,A)$ which contain a loop of X; whereas the kernel of ∂_* is the set of path components of $F^1(X,A)$ which contain paths whose end points are in the identity of $\pi_0(A)$, i.e., may be joined to x by a path in A. So Image $j_* \subset$ Kernel ∂_* is obvious; and for the opposite inequality, it is merely necessary to show that if

$$f(0) = x \qquad f(1) = a \in A$$
$$g(0) = a \qquad g(1) = x \qquad\qquad g(t) \in A$$

then $\exists\ F: I \times I \to X$ such that

$$F(0,t) = f(t) * e_a$$
$$F(t,0) = x$$
$$F(t,1) \in A$$
$$F(1,1) = x$$

F is provided by $F(s,t) = f(t) * g(st)$, and shows that every path in $F^1(X,A)$ whose end point can be joined to x by a path in A is homotopic in (X,A) to a loop of X. It follows that Kernel $\partial_* \subset$ Image j_*

Ⓒ Kernel $i_* =$ Image ∂_*

Let $\alpha \in \pi_0(A)$; so α is a path component of A. Then for $\alpha \in$ Kernel i_*, it is necessary and sufficient that the elements of α be elements of $C(x)$ in X. On the other hand, for $\alpha \in$ Image ∂_* it is necessary and sufficient that the elements of α be end points of paths which start at x; that is, the elements of α must be points of $C(x)$. This completes the proof.

THEOREM 1.6.13. *The sequence*

$$\cdots \to \pi_{n+1}(X,A) \xrightarrow{\partial_*} \pi_n(A) \xrightarrow{i_*} \pi_n(X) \xrightarrow{j_*} \pi_n(X,A) \to \cdots$$

is exact.

PROOF. The proof follows immediately from Lemmas 1.6.n; $n = 10$, 11, 12. In Lemma 1.6.12, we simply put $X = X^k$, $A = A^k$, then apply the other two.

THEOREM 1.6.14. *Let $B \subset A \subset X$, and let $k:(A,x) \subset (A,B)$, $\bar{i}:(A,B) \subset (X,B)$, $\bar{j}:(X,B) \subset (X,A)$ and let $\bar{\partial}_* = k_* \circ \partial_*$. Then the sequence*

$$\to \pi_{n+1}(X,A) \xrightarrow{\bar{\partial}_*} \pi_n(A,B) \xrightarrow{\bar{i}_*} \pi_n(X,B) \xrightarrow{\bar{j}_*} \pi_n(X,A) \to$$

is exact.

PROOF. See Eilenberg and Steenrod [B.3, p. 25, Theorem 10.2]. The theorem is there proved for homology; however, only his axioms 1, 2, 3, and 4 are used [see B.3, pp. 10, 11], all of which hold for homotopy as well, as we have proved. The proof thus goes through in exactly the same way.

PROBLEM 2. Let X be an $lc^{\frac{1}{2}}$, pathwise connected space, with $\tilde{X}$ a covering space of X. Then $\pi_n(\tilde{X}) \approx \pi_n(X)$, $n \geq 2$.

PROBLEM 3. Let $y \in \dot{I}^{n+1}$, and assume $\pi_n(X,x) = 0$. Then every map of (I^{n+1},y) into (X,x) can be extended to a map of I^{n+1} into X.

PROBLEM 4. Let $\pi_n(X,A) = 0$. Then every map of $(J^n, \{1\} \times \dot{I}^n, y)$ into (X,A,x) has an extension $f: I^{n+1} \to X$ with $f(\{1\} \times I^n) \subset A$.

1.7 The Bundle $\pi_n(X,A)$

The definition of this bundle corresponds to that of $\pi_n(X)$, and many of the lemmas in this case have proofs similar to those with the same number in Section 1.5. When this is so, the proof will be omitted.

Note, however, that these lemmas are not consequences of those of Section 1.5. For the bundle $\pi_n(X,A)$ is a bundle on A, not on X; and if we let $A = (x)$, so that $\pi_n(X,A,x) = \pi_n(X,x)$, then we have that the bundle $\pi_n(X,A)$ is a trivial bundle on a single point. The two cases then have to be stated separately.

Let

$$G^n(X,A) = \bigcup_{x \in A} F^n(X,A,x)$$

Define $\pi: G^n(X,A) \to A$ by $\pi(f) = x$ if $f \in F^n(X,A,x)$. Then we have the following theorem.

THEOREM 1.7.1. *π is continuous.*

DEFINITION. *Let $f \in F^n(X,A,x)$, $g \in F^n(X,A,b)$, and $p \in F^1(X,a,b)$. Then we say that $f \underset{p}{\equiv} g$ if and only if there exists a path P in $G^n(X,A)$ from f to g such that $\pi \circ P = p$. (Alternatively, there exists a map $P^*: I^{n+1} \to X$, such that $P^*(0,u) = f(u)$, $P^*(1,u) = g(u)$, $P^*(t,u) \in A$ if $n \in I^{n-1} \times \{1\}$, $P^*(t,u) = p(t)$ if $u \in J^{n-1}$.)*

DEFINITION. *Let $t \in I^n$. Then*

$$\|t\| = \max(|2t_1 - 1|,\cdots,|2t_{n-1} - 1|,1 - t_n)$$

LEMMA 1.7.2. *$\|t\| = 0$ if and only if $t = (\frac{1}{2},\cdots,\frac{1}{2},1)$*

$\|t\| = 1$ if and only if $t \in J^{n-1}$

DEFINITION. *Let $g \in F^n(X,A,y)$, $p \in F^1(A,x,y)$. Then*

$$\bar{\iota}_p(g)(t_1,\cdots,t_n) = \begin{cases} g(2t_1 - \frac{1}{2},\cdots,2t_{n-1} - \frac{1}{2},2t_n - 1), & 0 \le \|t\| \le \frac{1}{2} \\ p(2 - 2\|t\|), & \frac{1}{2} \le \|t\| \le 1 \end{cases}$$

An idea of what the map looks like is suggested by the picture.

LEMMA 1.7.3. *$(g,p) \to \bar{\iota}_p(g)$ is continuous from*

$$\bigcup_{x,y \in A} F^n(X,A,y) \times F^1(A,x,y)$$

to $G^n(X,A)$.

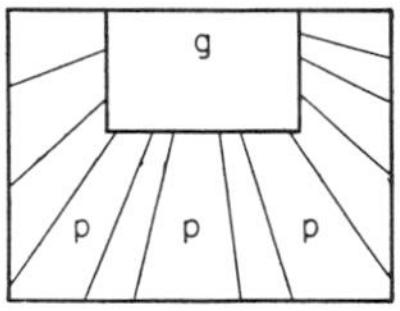

THEOREM 1.7.4. *If $g \equiv g'$ in $F^n(X,A,y)$ and $p \equiv p'$ in $F^1(A,x,y)$, then $\bar{\iota}_p(g) \equiv \bar{\iota}_{p'}(g')$ in $F^n(X,A,x)$.*

LEMMA 1.7.5. *$f \underset{p}{\equiv} g$, $g \underset{q}{\equiv} h \Rightarrow f \underset{pq}{\equiv} h$.*

LEMMA 1.7.6. $f \underset{p}{\equiv} g \Rightarrow g \underset{\hat{p}}{\equiv} f.$

LEMMA 1.7.7. $f \underset{p}{\equiv} f',\ p \equiv p'$ *in* $F^1(A,x,y) \Rightarrow f \underset{p'}{\equiv} f'.$

LEMMA 1.7.8. $f \underset{p}{\equiv} g,\ f' \underset{p}{\equiv} g \Rightarrow f \equiv f'$ *in* $F^n(X,A,x).$

LEMMA 1.7.9. $\bar{\imath}_p(g) \underset{p}{\equiv} g.$

COROLLARY 1.7.10. $f \underset{p}{\equiv} g$ *if and only if* $f \equiv \bar{\imath}_p(g)$ *in* $F^n(X,A,x).$

LEMMA 1.7.11. $f \underset{p}{\equiv} g,\ f' \underset{p}{\equiv} g' \Rightarrow f + f' \underset{p}{\equiv} g + g'.$

COROLLARY 1.7.12. $\bar{\imath}_p(g + g') \equiv \bar{\imath}_p(g) + \bar{\imath}_p(g')$ *in* $F^n(X,A,x).$

LEMMA 1.7.13. $\bar{\imath}_{e_a}(f) \equiv f$ *in* $F^n(X,A,x).$

LEMMA 1.7.14. $\bar{\imath}_{pq}(h) \equiv \bar{\imath}_p(\bar{\imath}_q(h))$ *in* $F^n(X,A,x).$

Thus if $\xi \in \pi_1(A,x,y)$, $\alpha \in \pi_n(X,A,y)$, then we may define $\bar{\theta}_\xi(\alpha) \in \pi_n(X,A,x)$ to be the path component of $\bar{\imath}_p(g)$ for any $p \in \xi$, $g \in \alpha$. Then we have the following Lemma.

LEMMA 1.7.15.
$$\begin{aligned} \bar{\theta}_\xi(\alpha + \alpha') &= \bar{\theta}_\xi(\alpha) + \bar{\theta}_\xi(\alpha') \\ \bar{\theta}_{\xi\eta}(\alpha) &= \bar{\theta}_\xi(\bar{\theta}_\eta(\alpha)) \\ \bar{\theta}_{\epsilon_y}(\alpha) &= \alpha \end{aligned}$$

COROLLARY 1.7.16. $\bar{\theta}_\xi$ *is a homomorphism from* $\pi_n(X,A,y)$ *to* $\pi_n(X,A,x).$

THEOREM 1.7.17. *If* A *is* 0-*connected, then the system* $\pi_n(X,A) = \{\pi_n(X,A,x),\bar{\theta}_\xi\}$ *is a bundle of groups in* A.

DEFINITION. *If* A *is* 0-*connected, the pair* (X,A) *is said to be n-simple if and only if the bundle* $\pi_n(X,A)$ *is simple.*

PROBLEM 5. Let $\alpha,\beta \in \pi_2(X,A,x)$; then
$$\bar{\theta}_{\partial_*(\alpha)}(\beta) = \alpha + \beta - \alpha$$

(Note that this group is not necessarily commutative, so that we do not necessarily have $\alpha + \beta - \alpha = \beta$.)

COROLLARY 1.7.18. *The kernel of*

$$\partial_*: \pi_2(X,A,x) \longrightarrow \pi_1(A,x)$$

is contained in the center of $\pi_2(X,A,x)$.

PROOF. Let $\alpha \in$ Kernel ∂_*. Then for $\beta \in \pi_2(X,A)$ we have $\alpha + \beta - \alpha = \bar{\theta}_{\partial_*(\alpha)}(\beta) = \theta_0(\beta) = \beta$. So $\alpha + \beta = \beta + \alpha$, and it follows that $\alpha \in$ center of $\pi_2(X,A,x)$.

DEFINITION. $\bar{\Omega}_n(X,A,x_0)$ *is the subgroup of* $\pi_n(X,A,x_0)$ *generated by all elements of the form* $\alpha - \bar{\theta}_\xi(\alpha)$, $\alpha \in \pi_n(X,A,x_0)$, $\xi \in \pi_1(A,x_0)$.

THEOREM 1.7.19. *If* $\xi \in \pi_1(A,x,y)$, *then* $\bar{\theta}_\xi(\bar{\Omega}_n(X,A,y)) \subset \Omega_n(X,A,x)$. *The system* $\{\bar{\Omega}_n(X,A,x), \theta_\xi | \bar{\Omega}_n(X,A,y)\} = \bar{\Omega}_n(X,A)$ *is a normal subbundle of* $\pi_n(X,A)$. *The bundle* $\pi_n(X,A)/\bar{\Omega}_n(X,A)$, *denoted by* $\pi_n^*(X,A)$, *is simple.*

PROOF. We first prove the following Lemma.

LEMMA 1.7.20. $\bar{\Omega}_n(X,A,x)$ *is a normal subgroup of* $\pi_n(X,A,x)$. *In particular,* $\bar{\Omega}_2(X,A,x)$ *contains the commutator subgroup of* $\pi_2(X,A,x)$.

PROOF. Since $\pi_n(X,A,x)$ is abelian for $n > 2$, we may confine our attention to the case of $n = 2$. We then have, for $\beta \in \pi_2(X,A,x)$, $\beta + (\alpha - \bar{\theta}_\xi(\alpha)) - \beta$

$$\begin{aligned}
&= \beta + \alpha - \beta + (\beta - \bar{\theta}_\xi(\alpha) - \beta) \\
&= \bar{\theta}_{\partial^*(\beta)}(\alpha) - \theta_{\partial^*(\beta)}(\bar{\theta}_\xi(\alpha)) \qquad \text{(by Problem 6)} \\
&= \bar{\theta}_{\partial^*(\beta)}(\alpha) - \bar{\theta}_{\partial^*(\beta)\cdot\xi}(\alpha) \qquad \text{(by Lemma 1.7.15)} \\
&= \bar{\theta}_{\partial^*(\beta)}(\alpha) - \bar{\theta}_{\partial^*(\beta)\xi[\partial^*(\beta)]^{-1}\partial^*(\beta)}(\alpha) \\
&= \bar{\theta}_{\partial^*(\beta)}(\alpha) - \bar{\theta}_{\partial^*(\beta)\xi[\partial^*(\beta)]^{-1}}(\bar{\theta}_{\partial^*(\beta)}(\alpha)) \in \bar{\Omega}_2(X,A,x)
\end{aligned}$$

This proves normality.

For the second statement, let $\alpha + \beta - \alpha - \beta$ be a generator of the commutator subgroup. Then

$$\begin{aligned}
\alpha + \beta - \alpha - \beta &= \bar{\theta}_{\partial^*(\alpha)}(\beta) - \beta \\
&= [\beta - \bar{\theta}_{\partial^*(\alpha)}(\beta)]^{-1} \in \bar{\Omega}_2(X,A,x_0)
\end{aligned}$$

This completes the proof of the lemma. The remainder of the proof of Theorem 1.7.19 is similar to the corresponding part of that of Theorem 1.5.18.

REMARK 1.7.21. *Let $f:(Y,B) \to (X,A)$. Then f_* maps $\pi_n(Y,B)$ homomorphically into $f^*\pi_n(X,A)$. That is to say: For $\xi \in \pi_1(B,x,y)$, $\alpha \in \pi_n(Y,B,y)$, we have*

$$f_*(\bar{\theta}_\xi(\alpha)) = \bar{\theta}_{f_*(\xi)}(f_*(\alpha))$$

DEFINITION. *Let $\xi \in \pi_1(A,x)$, $\alpha \in \pi_1(X,x)$, $i:(A,x) \to (X,x)$ be the inclusion map. Then $\bar{\theta}_\xi(\alpha) = \theta_{i_*\xi}(\alpha)$.*

THEOREM 1.7.22. *The diagram*

$$\begin{array}{ccccccccccc}
\cdots & \longrightarrow & \pi_{n+1}(X,A,x_0) & \xrightarrow{\partial_*} & \pi_n(A,x_0) & \xrightarrow{i_*} & \pi_n(X,x_0) & \xrightarrow{j_*} & \pi_n(X,A,x_0) & \longrightarrow & \cdots \\
 & & \downarrow{\scriptstyle \bar{\theta}_\xi} & & \downarrow{\scriptstyle \theta_\xi} & & \downarrow{\scriptstyle \theta'_\xi} & & \downarrow{\scriptstyle \bar{\theta}_\xi} & & \\
\cdots & \longrightarrow & \pi_{n+1}(X,A,x_0) & \xrightarrow{\partial_*} & \pi_n(A,x_0) & \xrightarrow{i_*} & \pi_n(X,x_0) & \xrightarrow{j_*} & \pi_n(X,A,x_0) & \longrightarrow & \cdots
\end{array}$$

is commutative.

PROOF. 1. Clearly $\bar{\partial} t_p(g) = t_p(\bar{\partial} g)$.
Therefore $\partial_* \circ \bar{\theta}_\xi = \theta_\xi \circ \partial_*$.
2. By Remark 1.5.20, we have

$$i_*(\theta_\xi(\alpha)) = \theta_{i_*\xi}(i_*(\alpha)) = \theta'_\xi(i_*(\alpha))$$

3. It is clearly sufficient to show that $t_p(g)$ and $\bar{t}_p(g)$ can be joined by a path in $F^n(X,A,x_0)$. By Corollary 1.7.10, it is sufficient to show that $t_p(g) \underset{p}{\equiv} g$ in the sense of Section 1.7, that is, that there exists a path P in $G^n(X,A)$ joining $t_p(g)$ to g, with $\pi \circ P = p$. Now there does exist such a path in $G^n(X)$. But clearly $G^n(X) \subset G^n(X,A)$. This completes the proof.

2. Homology and Homotopy

So far we have made no attempt to compute homotopy groups. In general, this is a problem of the utmost difficulty. In the current chapter we shall derive relationships between the homotopy and the singular homology groups, which will allow us to compute some homotopy groups. More precise relationships will be established in Chapter 3.

2.1 The Homology-Homotopy Ladder [6, 19]

We recall some of the definitions of cubical singular theory. Let $\alpha_i^\epsilon : I^{n-1} \to I^n$, $\beta_i : I^n \to I^{n-1}$ be the maps given by

$$\begin{cases} \alpha_i^\epsilon(t_1, \cdots, t_{n-1}) = (t_1, \cdots, t_{i-1}, \epsilon, t_i, \cdots, t_{n-1}) & (i = 1, \cdots, n;\ \epsilon = 0, 1) \\ \beta_i(t_1, \cdots, t_n) = (t_1, \cdots, \hat{t}_i, \cdots, t_n) & (i = 1, \cdots, n) \end{cases}$$

Note the formulas:

$$\alpha_j^\eta \circ \alpha_i^\epsilon = \alpha_{i+1}^\epsilon \circ \alpha_j^\eta \qquad (j \leq i) \tag{C.1}$$

$$\beta_j \circ \alpha_i^\epsilon = \begin{cases} \alpha_{i-1}^\epsilon \circ \beta_j & (j < i) \\ \text{identity} & (j = i) \\ \alpha_i^\epsilon \circ \beta_{j-1} & (j > i) \end{cases} \tag{C.2}$$

$$\beta_i \circ \beta_j = \beta_j \circ \beta_{i+1} \qquad (i \geq j) \tag{C.3}$$

A *singular* n-cube in a space X is a map $f: I^n \to X$. The free abelian group whose basis is the set of all singular cubes in X is called $Q_n(X)$; evidently

$$Q(X) = \sum_{n=0}^{\infty} \oplus\ Q_n(X)$$

where $Q_n(X)$ is the subgroup spanned by the n-cubes.

The n-cube $f: I^n \to X$ is *degenerate* if and only if $\exists$ an $(n-1)$-cube $g: I^{n-1} \to X$, such that $f = g \circ \beta_n$. The cube g is then uniquely determined; in fact, $g = f \circ \alpha_n^0 = f \circ \alpha_n^1$. For $n > 0$ this means that f does not depend on its last coordinate.

Define $\partial: Q(X) \to Q(X)$ by

$$\partial f = \sum_{i=1}^{n} (-1)^{i+1}(f \circ \alpha_i^1 - f \circ \alpha_i^0)$$

for every singular n-cube f. Then $\partial(Q_n(X)) \subset Q_{n-1}(X)$ and $\partial \cdot \partial = 0$, by formulas C.1 through C.3. Hence $Q(X)$ is an abstract complex.

Suppose that f is degenerate, $f = g \circ \beta_n = f \circ \alpha_n^0 \circ \beta_n$. Then, if $i < n$,

$$f \circ \alpha_i^\epsilon = g \circ \beta_n \circ \alpha_i^\epsilon = g \circ \alpha_i^\epsilon \circ \beta_{n-1}$$

while

$$f \circ \alpha_n^\epsilon = g \circ \beta_n \circ \alpha_n^\epsilon = g$$

Thus $f \circ \alpha_i^\epsilon$ is degenerate for $i < n$, while $f \circ \alpha_n^1 = f \circ \alpha_n^0 (= g)$, and therefore ∂f is a linear combination of degenerate cubes. Letting $D(X) =$ the subgroup of $Q(X)$ generated by all degenerate cubes, we have

1. $D(X) = \sum \oplus D(X) \cap Q_n(X) = \sum \oplus D_n(X)$
2. $D(X)$ is a subcomplex of $Q(X)$

Hence we may define the *total cubical complex* $C(X) = Q(X)/D(X)$; $C(X) = \sum \oplus C_n(X)$ where $C_n(X) \approx Q_n(X)/D_n(X)$. If $A \subset X$, then $D(A) = Q(A) \cap D(X)$, and $\partial Q(A) \subset Q(A)$. Hence we may regard $C(A)$ as a subcomplex of $C(X)$. The complex $C(X)$ is free, with a basis consisting of the cosets of the *nondegenerate* singular cubes; hence, if G is any abelian group, $C(A) \otimes G$ is a subcomplex of $C(X) \otimes G$, and we may define $H_q(X,A;G)$ to be the qth homology group of the complex $C(X) \otimes G/C(A) \otimes G$. Similarly, we may define the cohomology groups $H^q(X,A;G)$. It can be verified that these groups are isomorphic with the singular homology and cohomology groups, based on singular simplexes [6].

LEMMA 2.1.1. *If $c \in Q(X)$, denote by $[c]$ the coset $c + D(X)$. Let $i_n: I^n \to I^n$ be the identity map, and denote by ω_n the class of $[i_n]$ in the relative homology group $H_n(I^n, \dot{I}^n)$. Then ω_n generates $H_n(I^n, \dot{I}^n)$, an infinite cyclic group.*

PROOF. The fact that $H_n(I^n, \dot{I}^n)$ is an infinite cyclic group is well known. The fact that ω_n generates it corresponds precisely to the fact that the identity map of an n-simplex σ generates the singular homology group $H_n(\sigma, \dot{\sigma})$. We outline the proof, which is by induction on n.

a. $n = 0$. In this case i_0 is the only cell, so clearly the class of $[i_0]$ must generate $H_0(I^0,\dot{I}^0)$.

b. Assume ω_{n-1} generates $H_{n-1}(I^{n-1},\dot{I}^{n-1})$. Let $I^n_{i,\epsilon} = \alpha^\epsilon_i(I^{n-1})_1$. Consider the diagram

$$\begin{array}{ccc} H_{n-1}(I^{n-1},\dot{I}^{n-1}) \xrightarrow{\alpha_{n*}} H_{n-1}(I^{n-1}_{n,1},\dot{I}^{n-1}_{n,1}) = & H_{n-1}(I^{n-1}_{n,1},J^{n-1} \cap I^{n-1}_{n,1}) \\ & \downarrow e_* \\ H_n(I^n,\dot{I}^n) \xrightarrow{\partial_*} H_{n-1}(\dot{I}^n) \xrightarrow{j_*} H_{n-1}(\dot{I}^n,J^{n-1}) = & H_{n-1}(J^{n-1} \cup I^{n-1}_{n,1},J^{n-1}) \end{array}$$

Note that e_* is an excision isomorphism.

All mappings are isomorphisms onto (j_* because J^{n-1} is contractable, others trivially). The mapping α^1_{n*} takes ω_{n-1}, which is induced by i_{n-1}, into the element ω'_{n-1} induced by $\alpha^1_n:I^{n-1} \rightarrow I^{n-1}_{n,1}$. A moment's reflection on the nature of the excision isomorphism will yield the result that $e_*(\omega'_{n-1}) = \omega''_{n-1}$ is induced by the map $\alpha^1_n:I^{n-1} \rightarrow \dot{I}^n$. Now $\alpha^\epsilon_i(I^{n-1}) \subset J^{n-1}$ whenever $i < n$ or $\epsilon = 0$. It follows that

$$\sum_{i=1}^{n-1} (-1)^{i+1}([\alpha^1_i] - [\alpha^0_i]) - (-1)^{n+1}[\alpha^0_n] \equiv 0 \bmod C(J^{n-1})$$

so that

$$\sum_{i=1}^{n} (-1)^{i+1}([\alpha^1_i] - [\alpha^0_i]) \equiv (-1)^{n+1}[\alpha^1_n] \bmod C(J^{n-1})$$

It follows that ω''_{n-1} is induced also by the chain

$$(-1)^{n+1} \sum_{i=1}^{n} (-1)^{i+1}([\alpha^1_i] - [\alpha^0_i]) = A_n(-1)^{n+1}$$

Since j_* is induced by the identity mapping, the chain $A_n(-1)^{n+1}$ induces $\omega'''_{n-1} = j_*^{-1}(\omega''_{n-1})$ as well. Now

$$[\partial i_n] = \sum_{i=1}^{n} (-1)^{i+1}([i_n \circ \alpha^1_i] - [i_n \circ \alpha^0_i])$$

so that clearly $\partial_*\omega_n$ is induced by A_n. The chain of isomorphisms therefore takes ω_{n-1} into $(-1)^{n+1}\omega_n$. Since this therefore generates $H_n(I^n,\dot{I}^n)$, so does ω_n. Q.E.D.

Now from reasoning similar to that of Theorem 1.04, it follows that, if $\alpha \in \pi_n(X,A,x)$ and $f,f' \in \alpha$, then $f_* = f'_*:H_n(I^n,\dot{I}^n) \rightarrow H_n(X,A)$. Hence we may define a function

$$\rho:\pi_n(X,A,x) \rightarrow H_n(X,A)$$

by $\rho(\alpha) = f_*(\omega_n)$ for any $f \in \alpha$. Explicitly, f is a singular cube in X whose boundary is a singular chain of A, so $[f] \in Z_n(X,A)$, and $\rho_*(\alpha)$ is the homology class of $[f]$.

THEOREM 2.1.2. *$\rho:\pi_n(X,A,x) \to H_n(X,A)$ is a homomorphism.*

PROOF. We first need some auxiliary lemmas.
Let

$$I^n_- = \{t \in I^n | 0 \leq t_n \leq \tfrac{1}{2}\}$$
$$I^n_+ = \{t \in I^n | \tfrac{1}{2} \leq t_n \leq 1\}$$
$$K^{n-1} = \dot{I}^n_+ \cup \dot{I}^n_-$$

Let ζ_+,ζ_- be the inclusion maps $(I^n_+,\dot{I}^n_+) \to (I^n,K^{n-1})(I^n_-,\dot{I}^n_-) \to (I^n,K^{n-1})$.

LEMMA 2.1.3. *ζ_+ and ζ_- induce an isomorphism onto:*

$$\zeta_*: H_n(I^n_+,\dot{I}^n_+) \oplus H_n(I^n_-,\dot{I}^n_-) \approx H_n(I^n,K^{n-1})$$

given by $\zeta_*(a \oplus b) = \zeta_{+*}(a) + \zeta_{-*}(b)$.

PROOF. Since I^n, I^n_+, and I^n_- are contractible, it suffices to prove that

$$H_{n-1}(\dot{I}^n_+) \oplus H_{n-1}(\dot{I}^n_-) \approx H_{n-1}(K^{n-1})$$

under the inclusion maps. But $\dot{I}^n_+ \cap \dot{I}^n_-$ is the $(n-1)$-cell

$$\{t \in I^n | t_1 = \tfrac{1}{2}\}$$

and therefore is contractable. Hence our result follows from the Mayer-Vietoris theorem, since $\dot{I}^n_+$ and $\dot{I}^n_-$ are neighborhood deformation retracts of K^{n-1}.

LEMMA 2.1.4. *Let f_+, f_- be maps of $(I^n,\dot{I}^n,J^{n-1})$ into (X,A,x) such that $f_+(I^n_-) = f_-(I^n_+) = \{x\}$, and let $g:(I^n,\dot{I}^n,J^{n-1}) \to (X,A,x)$ be the map such that*

$$g|I^n_+ = f_+|I^n_+$$
$$g|I^n_- = f_-|I^n_-$$

Then

$$g_*(\omega_n) = f_{+*}(\omega_n) + f_{-*}(\omega_n) \in H_n(X,A)$$

PROOF. By Lemma 2.1.3, we have

$$\eta_*\omega_n = \zeta_{+*}(\omega_+) + \zeta_{-*}(\omega_-)$$

where $\eta:(I^n,\dot{I}^n) \subset (I^n,K^{n-1})$. Now let $g_1:(I^n,K^{n-1}) \to (X,A)$ be the map defined by g. Then

$$g_*(\omega_n) = g_{1*}(\eta_*(\omega_n)) = g_*\zeta_{+*}\omega_+ + g_*\zeta_{-*}\omega_-$$

But $g \circ \zeta_+ = f_+ \circ \zeta_+$ and $g \circ \zeta_- = f_- \circ \zeta_-$. Hence

$$g_*(\omega_n) = f_{+*}\zeta_{+*}(\omega_+) + f_{-*}\zeta_{-*}(\omega_-)$$

But $f_+ \circ \zeta_-(I^n_-) \subset A$ and therefore $f_{+*} \circ \zeta_{-*} = 0$. Similarly $f_{-*} \circ \zeta_{+*} = 0$.

Hence

$$f_{+*}(\omega_n) = f_{+*}(\zeta_{+*}(\omega_+) + \zeta_{-*}(\omega_-))$$
$$= f_{+*}\zeta_{+*}(\omega_+)$$

and similarly

$$f_{-*}(\omega_n) = f_{-*}\zeta_{-*}(\omega_-)$$

Hence

$$g_*(\omega_n) = f_{+*}(\omega_n) + f_{-*}(\omega_n) \qquad \text{Q.E.D.}$$

PROOF OF THEOREM 2.1.2. Let $\alpha,\beta \in \pi_n(X,A,x)$ and let $g_+ \in \alpha$, $g_- \in \beta$, $g = g_+ + g_-$. Let $f_+ = g_+ + e_x$, $f_- = e_x + g_-$. Then f_+,f_-,g satisfy the hypotheses of Lemma 2.1.4. Hence

$$g_*\omega_n = f_{+*}\omega_n + f_{-*}\omega_n$$

But $f_+ \equiv g_+, f_- \equiv g_-$, whence

$$f_{+*}\omega_n = g_{+*}\omega_n$$
$$f_{-*}\omega_n = g_{-*}\omega_n$$

Hence

$$\rho(\alpha + \beta) = g_*\omega_n = g_{+*}\omega_n + g_{-*}\omega_n = \rho(\alpha) + \rho(\beta) \qquad \text{Q.E.D.}$$

Now consider the effect of ρ on the homotopy sequence.

THEOREM 2.1.5. *The diagram*

$$\begin{array}{ccccccccc} \cdots \longrightarrow & \pi_{n+1}(X,A,x) & \xrightarrow{\partial_*} & \pi_n(A,x) & \xrightarrow{i_*} & \pi_n(X,x) & \xrightarrow{j_*} & \pi_n(X,A,x) & \longrightarrow \cdots \\ & \downarrow \rho & & \downarrow \rho & & \downarrow \rho & & \downarrow \rho & \\ \cdots \longrightarrow & H_{n+1}(X,A) & \xrightarrow{\partial_*} & H_n(A,x) & \xrightarrow{i_*} & H_n(X,x) & \xrightarrow{j_*} & H_n(X,A) & \longrightarrow \cdots \end{array}$$

is a ladder; i.e., $\rho \circ \partial_* = \partial_* \circ \rho$, $\rho \circ i_* = i_* \circ \rho$, *and* $\rho \circ j_* = j_* \circ \rho$.

PROOF. Let $f \in \alpha \in \pi_n(X,A,x)$. Then

$$\rho(\alpha) = [f] + B_{n+1}(X,A)$$

and therefore $\partial_*\rho(\alpha) = [\partial f] + B_n(A,x)$. But $f \circ \alpha_i^\epsilon$ is degenerate unless $i = 1$, $\epsilon = 1$ (since $f(J^{n-1}) = \{x\}$), whence

$$\partial_*\rho(\alpha) = [f \circ \alpha_{n+1}^1] + B_n(A,x)$$

On the other hand, $\bar{\partial} f \in \partial_*\alpha$, whence

$$\rho(\partial_*\alpha) = [\bar{\partial} f] + B_n(A,x)$$
$$= [f \circ \alpha_{n+1}^1] + B_n(A,x)$$
$$= \partial_*\rho(\alpha)$$

whence the first equality holds.

To prove the second, let $f \in \alpha \in \pi_n(A,x)$ and let $f_1 = i \circ f:(I^n,\dot{I}^n) \to (X,x)$. Then $f_1 \in i_*\alpha \in \pi_n(X,x)$ and therefore

$$\rho i_*(\alpha) = [f_1] + B_n(X,x)$$

But

$$\begin{aligned} i_*\rho(\alpha) &= i_*\{[f] + B_n(A,x)\} \\ &= [f_1] + B_n(X,x) \end{aligned}$$

The proof of the third relation is similar.

The diagram of the foregoing theorem is called the *homotopy-homology ladder of* (X,A,x).

LEMMA 2.1.6. *The homomorphism* $\rho:\pi_n(X,A,x_0) \to H_n(X,A)$ *maps* $\bar{\Omega}_n(X,A,x_0)$ *into zero, and* $\rho:\pi_n(X,x_0) \to H_n(X,x_0)$ *maps* $\Omega_n(X,x_0)$ *into zero.*

PROOF. If $f,f' \in F^n(X,A,x_0)$ are representatives of α, $\theta_\xi(\alpha)$, and $p \in F^1(A,x_0,x_0)$ is a representative of ξ, then there is a map $F:I^{n+1} \to X$ such that

$$\begin{cases} \left.\begin{aligned} F(0,u) &= f(u) \\ F(1,u) &= f'(u) \end{aligned}\right\} & u \in I^n \\ F(t,u) \in A & u \in \dot{I}^n,\ t \in I \\ F(t,u) = p(t) & u \in J^{n-1},\ t \in I \end{cases}$$

Then $F:(I \times I^n, I \times \dot{I}^n) \to (X,A)$ and therefore

$$f_* = f'_*:H_n(I^n,\dot{I}^n) \to H_n(X,A)$$

Hence $\rho(\alpha) = f_*\omega_n = f'_*\omega_n = \rho(\theta_\xi(\alpha))$, $\rho(\alpha - \theta_\xi(\alpha)) = 0$, and it follows that $\rho\bar{\Omega}_n(X,A,x_0) = 0$. Similarly in the absolute case.

2.2 On $\pi_n(S^n)$ [29]

So far we have used a fixed reference cell I^n in defining the relative homotopy groups. For later purposes it will be desirable to allow ourselves greater latitude by replacing I^n by a homeomorph. For example, if E is an n-cell with boundary $\dot{E}$, and $y_0 \in \dot{E}$, and if $f:(E,\dot{E},y_0) \to (X,A,x_0)$ is a map, then for any $\phi \in F^n(E,\dot{E},y_0)$ we have $f \circ \phi \in F^n(X,A,x_0)$, and the correspondence $f \to f \circ \phi$ induces a map θ from the set of homotopy classes of maps of $(E,\dot{E},y_0)$ into (X,A,x_0) into $\pi_n(X,A,x_0)$. This map depends only on the element $\alpha \in \pi_n(E,\dot{E},y_0)$ represented by the map ϕ. If we choose ϕ so that $\phi|I^n - J^{n-1}$ is a homeomorphism then θ is 1:1 onto. Thus we may represent $\pi_n(X,A,x_0)$ as the set of homotopy classes of maps of $(E,\dot{E},y_0)$ into (X,A,x_0). In order to see how this representation depends on the choice of ϕ, we need to calculate $\pi_n(E,\dot{E},y_0)$. Since E is contractible, $\pi_n(E,\dot{E},y_0) \approx \pi_{n-1}(\dot{E},y_0)$. Accordingly our problem is to calculate the $(n-1)$st homotopy group of the $(n-1)$-sphere.

THEOREM 2.2.1. *Let S be an n-sphere, $y_0 \in S$. Then* $\rho:\pi_n(S,y_0) \to H_n(S,y_0)$ *is an isomorphism onto.*

The proof we give here is due to Whitney [29]. Clearly ρ is onto; for if $f:(I^n,\dot{I}^n) \to (S,y_0)$ is topological on $I^n - \dot{I}^n$, then $f_*:H_n(I^n,\dot{I}^n) \approx H_n(S,y_0)$. (See, for instance, Eilenberg and Steenrod [B.3, p. 266, Theorem 5.4] and the previous definitions and lemmas of that paragraph. Although that theorem applies only to Čech theory, it is applicable here, because the Čech theory and the ordinary theory coincide on triangulable spaces, and I^n, $\dot{I}^n$, S, and y_0 are all triangulable. It also follows from Lemma 2.6.3.)

Therefore, if α is the homotopy class of f, then $\rho(\alpha) = f_*(\omega_n)$ is a generator of $H_n(S^n,y_0)$.

In showing that ρ is an isomorphism, we may take $S = \dot{T}^{n+1}$, where T^{n+1} is a simplex with vertices $b_0, \cdots, b_{n+1}$. Let T^n_i be the face of T^{n+1} opposite to the vertex b_i. Let $f_0:(I^n,\dot{I}^n) \to (\dot{T}^{n+1},b_0)$ be a map with $f_{0*}\omega_n = 0$. By the simplicial approximation theorem, there is a simplicial decomposition (K,L) of $(I_n,\dot{I}^n)$ and a simplicial map $f_1:(K,L) \to (\dot{T}^{n+1},b_0)$ such that $f_0 \equiv f_1$ in $F^n(\dot{T}^{n+1},b_0)$.

Orient the n-simplexes $\sigma_1, \cdots, \sigma_N$ of K so that $\sum_{i=1}^N \sigma_i$ is a relative cycle of (K,L) whose homology class is ω_n. Orient T_0 by the given ordering $b_1, \cdots, b_{n+1}$ of its vertices. Suppose that $\sigma_1, \cdots, \sigma_p$ are the simplexes of K which are mapped by f_1 onto T_0, and that $\sigma_{p+1}, \cdots, \sigma_{p+q}$ are those which are mapped by f_1 onto $-T_0$. Then it is clear that $p = q$, since $f_{1*}\omega_n = 0$.

Define a map $\Delta:\dot{T}^{n+1} \times I \to \dot{T}^{n+1}$ as follows:

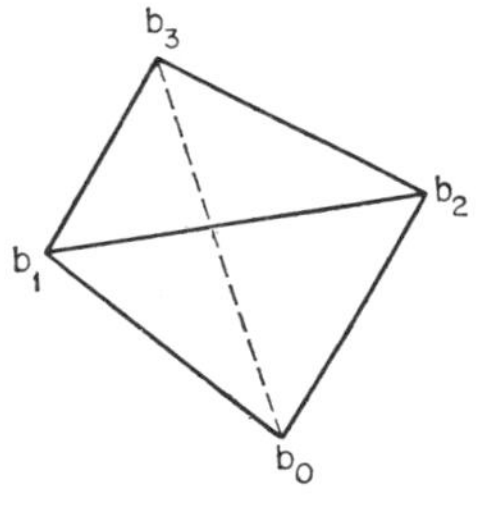

1. If $x \in \overline{\dot{T}^{n+1} - T^n_0}$, then $\Delta(x,t) = (1-t)x + tb_0$.
2. If $x \in T^n_0$, let $\lambda_1(x), \cdots, \lambda_{n+1}(x)$ be the barycentric coordinates of x with respect to $b_1, \cdots, b_{n+1}$; let $\lambda(x) = (n+1) \min \lambda_i(x)$, and let $b = [1/(n+1)] \sum b_i$ be the barycenter of T^n_0. Then

$$\Delta(x,t) = \begin{cases} (1+t)x - tb & \left(\dfrac{t}{1+t} \le \lambda(x) \le 1\right) \\ \dfrac{(1-t) + \lambda(x)(1+t)}{1-\lambda(x)}\{x - \lambda(x)b\} + \{t - \lambda(x)(1+t)\}b_0 & \\ & \left(0 \le \lambda(x) \le \dfrac{t}{1+t}\right) \end{cases}$$

Then $\Delta(x,0) = x$, and $\Delta(x,1) = b_0$ for $x \in \overline{\dot{T}^{n+1} - T^n_0}$, while $\Delta(b_0,t) = b_0$. Let $F:(\dot{T}^{n+1},b_0) \to (\dot{T}^{n+1},b_0)$ be defined by

$$F(x) = \Delta(x,1)$$

Then $f_2 = F \circ f_1$ is homotopic relative to $\dot{I}^n$ to f_1. Note that f_2 has the following property:

(*) If σ is a simplex of K which is mapped onto $\pm T_i^n (i \neq 0)$ by f_1 or is mapped degenerately by f_1, then $f_2(\sigma) = b_0$.

Let us call a map $f:(I^n,\dot{I}^n) \to (\dot{T}^{n+1},b_0)$ *canonical* if and only if for every n-simplex $\sigma \in K$, either $f(\sigma) = b_0$, or $f|\sigma = F \circ \phi$, where ϕ is a simplicial map of σ onto $\pm T_0^n$. Note that, in the latter case, ϕ is uniquely determined by $f|\sigma$. We shall say that $f|\sigma$ is positive (negative) if and only if $\phi(\sigma) = T_0^n (\phi(\sigma) = -T_0^n)$.

We have shown that every map $f_0:(I^n,\dot{I}^n) \to (\dot{T}^{n+1},b_0)$ is homotopic, relative to $\dot{I}^{n+1}$, to a canonical map f_2. If $f_{0*}(\omega_n) = 0$, then f_2 has the following property.

(**) The number $p(f_2)$ of n-simplexes mapped positively by f_2 is equal to the number of n-simplexes mapped negatively by f_2.

We now prove by induction on $p(f_2)$:

(α): Let $f_2:(I^n,\dot{I}^n) \to (\dot{T}^{n+1},b)$ be a canonical map having the property (**). Then $f_2 \equiv e_{b_0}$ in $F^n(\dot{T}^{n+1},b_0)$.

Suppose $p(f_2) = 0$. Then f_2 is already constant. We now show that f_2 is homotopic to a canonical map f_3 such that $p(f_3) < p(f_2)$. For this we need some lemmas.

LEMMA 1. *Let T^n be an n-simplex, $f:T^n \to T_0^n$ a simplicial map, and let $\phi:T^n \to T^n$ be a simplicial map which induces an even permutation of the vertices of T^n. Then $F \circ f$ is homotopic, relative to $\dot{T}^n$, to $F \circ f \circ \phi$.*

PROOF. Since the alternating group is generated by the 3-cycles (abc), we may assume

$$\phi(a_1) = a_2,\ \phi(a_2) = a_3,\ \phi(a_3) = a_1,\ \phi(a_i) = a_i (i > 3)$$

Let T' be the face of T^n spanned by a_1, a_2, a_3, and let T'' be the face spanned by the remaining a_i. Define $\Phi':(T' \times I,\dot{T}' \times I) \to (T',\dot{T}')$ as follows. Let $\lambda_1(x)$, $\lambda_2(x)$, $\lambda_3(x)$ be the barycentric coordinates of x with respect to a_1, a_2, a_3. Then if

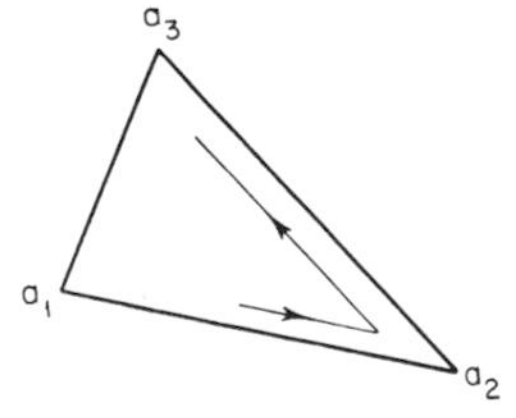

$$\lambda_3(x) \leq \lambda_1(x), \qquad \lambda_3(x) \leq \lambda_2(x)$$

$$\Phi'(x,t) = \begin{cases} \{\lambda_1(x) - t(1 - 3\lambda_3(x))\}a_1 + \{\lambda_2(x) + t(1 - 3\lambda_3(x))\}a_2 \\ \quad + \lambda_3(x)a_3, \qquad \left(0 \leq t \leq \dfrac{\lambda_1(x) - \lambda_3(x)}{1 - 3\lambda_3(x)}\right) \\ \lambda_3(x)a_1 + \{\lambda_1(x) + (1 - t)(1 - 3\lambda_3(x))\}a_2 + \{\lambda_2(x) \\ \quad - (1 - t)(1 - 3\lambda_3(x))\}a_3, \qquad \left(\dfrac{\lambda_1(x) - \lambda_3(x)}{1 - 3\lambda_3(x)} \leq t \leq 1\right) \end{cases}$$

If $\lambda_1(x) \leq \lambda_2(x)$, $\lambda_1(x) \leq \lambda_3(x)$

$$\Phi'(x,t) = \phi(\Phi'(\phi^{-1}(x),t))$$

If $\lambda_2(x) \leq \lambda_1(x)$, $\lambda_2(x) \leq \lambda_3(x)$

$$\Phi'(x,t) = \phi(\Phi'(\phi^{-1}(x),t)) = \phi^2(\Phi'(\phi^{-2}(x),t))$$

Then define $\Phi:(T^n \times I,\dot{T}^n \times I) \to (T^n,\dot{T}^n)$ by

$$\Phi((1 - \lambda)x' + \lambda x'',t) = (1 - \lambda)\Phi'(x',t) + \lambda x'' \qquad (x' \in T',x'' \in T'',\lambda \in I)$$

Then Φ is a homotopy of the identity to ϕ. Hence $F \circ f$ is homotopic relative to $\dot{T}^n$ to $F \circ f \circ \phi$ under the homotopy $F \circ f \circ \Phi$.

LEMMA 2. *Let T_-, T_+ be positively oriented simplexes of K such that $T_+ \cap T_-$ is an $(n-1)$-simplex T^{n-1}, and let $T = T_- \cup T_+$. Let $f:T_- \to T_0^n$ be a positive simplicial map, and let $g:(T,\dot{T}) \to (\dot{T}^{n+1},b_0)$ be the map defined by*

$$g(x) = \begin{cases} F(f(x)) & x \in T_- \\ b_0 & x \in T_+ \end{cases}$$

Then g is homotopic, relative to $\dot{T}$, to a map g' such that

$$g'(x) = \begin{cases} b_0 & x \in T_- \\ F(f'(x)) & x \in T_+ \end{cases}$$

where $f':T_+ \to T_0^n$ is a positive simplicial map.

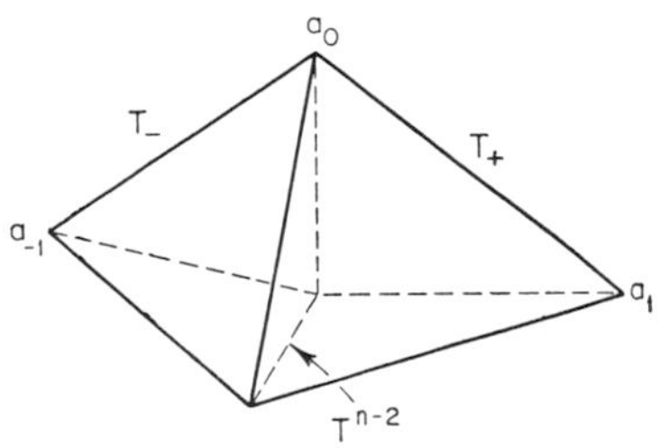

PROOF. Let T^{n-2} be a face of T^{n-1}, a_0 the vertex of T^{n-1} opposite T^{n-2}, a_{-1} and a_1 the vertices of T_- and T_+ opposite T^{n-1}. For $-1 \leq \lambda \leq 1$, let

$$a_\lambda = \begin{cases} (1 + \lambda)a_0 - \lambda a_{-1} & (-1 \leq \lambda \leq 0) \\ (1 - \lambda)a_0 + \lambda a_1 & (0 \leq \lambda \leq 1) \end{cases}$$

For $x \in T$, we have

$$x = (1 - \mu)a_\lambda + \mu y \qquad (-1 \le \lambda \le 1, \mu \in I, y \in T^{n-2})$$

Define

$$G(x,t) = \begin{cases} b_0 & (-1 \le \lambda \le t - 1) \\ F\{f((1 - \mu)a_{\lambda - t} + \mu y))\cdot & (t - 1 \le \lambda \le t) \\ b_0 & (t \le \lambda \le 1) \end{cases}$$

If $f'(x) = f((1 - \lambda)a_{\lambda-1} + \mu y)$ for $x \in T_+$, then f' is a positive simplicial map and G is a homotopy of g to g'.

LEMMA 3. *Let T_-, T_+, T be as in Lemma 2, and let $f:T_- \to T_0^n, f':T_+ \to T_0^n$ be simplicial maps with f positive, f' negative. Then if $g:(T,\dot{T}) \to (\dot{T}^{n+1},b_0)$ is the map defined by*

$$(***) \qquad g(x) = \begin{cases} F(f(x)) & x \in T_- \\ F(f'(x)) & x \in T_+ \end{cases}$$

then g is homotopic, relative to $\dot{T}$, to the constant map of T into b_0.

PROOF. There is a positive simplicial map $\phi:T_- \to T_-$ such that $f_1 = f \circ \phi$ agrees with f' on T^{n-1}. Then by Lemma 1, g is homotopic, relative to T, to the map g_1 defined by (***) with f_1 in place of f. Define $H:(T \times I, \dot{T} \times I) \to (\dot{T}^{n+1},b_0)$ by

$$H(x,t) = \begin{cases} F\{f_1((1 - t)x + ta_{-1})\} & x \in T_- \\ F\{f'((1 - t)x + ta_1)\} & x \in T_+ \end{cases}$$

We must check that H is well defined on $T_- \cap T_+ = T^{n-1}$. To this end, let $\psi:T_- \to T_+$ be the simplicial map defined by $\psi(a_{-1}) = a_1$, $\psi|T^{n-1} =$ identity. Then $f_1 = f' \circ \psi$; now since f_1 and f' are positive and negative respectively, their images must be $\pm T_0^n$; it follows that $f_1(a_{-1}) \notin f_1(T^{n-1})$, $f'(a_1) \notin f'(T^{n-1}) = f_1(T^{n-1})$; furthermore, $f_1(T^{n-1}) = f'(T^{n-1})$ must actually be an $(n - 1)$-subsimplex of T_0^n, for the same reason. There is therefore only one vertex left for both $f'(a_1)$ and $f_1(a_{-1})$. So $f_1(a_{-1}) = f'(a_1) = f'(\psi(a_{-1})) = (f' \circ \psi)(a_{-1})$. But clearly $f_1|T^{n-1} = f' \circ \psi|T^{n-1}$; and so, since f_1 and $f' \circ \psi$ are both simplicial, we have $f_1 = f' \circ \psi$. ψ, being simplicial, takes $(1 - t)x + ta_{-1}$ into $(1 - t)x + ta_1$ for $x \in T^{n-1}$; and since $f_1 = f' \circ \psi$, the proof of consistency is completed.

We can now prove (α). As we have seen, it suffices to prove that f_2 is homotopic to a canonical map f_3 with $p(f_3) < p(f_2)$. Let T', T'' be simplexes of K such that f_2 is positive on T', negative on T''. Since I^n is a bounded pseudomanifold, $\exists$ a sequence $T_0 = T', T_1, \cdots, T_{m-1}, T_m = T''$ of n-simplexes of K such that T_i and T_{i+1} have an $(n - 1)$ face in common $(i = 0, \cdots, m - 1)$. Shortening this chain if necessary, we may assume that $f_2(T_i) = b_0 (i = 1, \cdots, m - 1)$. By Lemma 2, f_2 is homotopic, relative to K^{n-1}, to a map $f_2^{(1)}$ such that $f_2^{(1)}(T_0) = b_0$ and

$f_2^{(1)}$ is positive on T_1, while $f_2^{(1)} = f_2$ on the remaining simplexes of K. By repeated application of Lemma 2, we see that f_2 is homotopic, relative to K^{n-1}, to a map $f_2^{(m-1)}$ such that $f_2^{(m-1)}$ is positive on T_{m-1}, $f_2^{(m-1)}(T_0) = b_0$, and $f_2^{(m-1)} = f_2$ on the remaining simplexes of K. By Lemma 3, $f_2^{(m-1)}$ is homotopic, relative to K^{n-1}, to a map f_3 such that $f_3(T_{m-1}) = f_3(T_m) = b_0$ and $f_3 = f_2$ on the remaining simplexes of K. Then $p(f_3) = p(f_2) - 1$, and we are through.

THEOREM 2.2.2. $\pi_p(S^{n-1}) = 0$ *for* $p < n - 1$.

PROOF. The proof is similar in principle to that of the previous theorem, although of course much simpler. Let $f:(I^p,\dot{I}^p) \to (\dot{I}^n,x)$, $p < n - 1$, where $x \in \dot{I}^n$ is arbitrary, and let (K_1,x) be an arbitrary simplicial decomposition of $(\dot{I}^n,x)$. By the simplicial approximation theorem, there is a simplicial decomposition (K,L) of $(I^p,\dot{I}^p)$ and a simplicial map $f_1:(K,L) \to (K_1,x)$ so that f_1 is homotopic to f relative to $|L| = \dot{I}^n$. Then $f_1(K) = f_1(K^p) \subset K_1^p$, which certainly does not exhaust the $(n-1)$-manifold $\dot{I}^n$. So f_1 misses at least one point and thus is homotopic relative to $\dot{I}^p$ to e_x. This completes the proof.

COROLLARY 2.2.3. *If E is an n-cell,* $y_0 \in \dot{E}$, *then* $\rho:\pi_n(E,\dot{E},y_0) \approx H_n(E,\dot{E})$.

Let E be an n-cell. By an *orientation* of E we mean a generator of $H_n(E,\dot{E})$. Let $y_0 \in \dot{E}$, let $f:(E,\dot{E},y_0) \to (X,A,x_0)$ be a map, and let ω be an orientation of E. Let $\phi:(I^n,\dot{I}^n,J^{n-1}) \to (E,\dot{E},y_0)$ be a map such that $\phi_*(\omega_n) = \omega$. By Corollary 2.2.3, if ϕ, ϕ' are any two such maps, then $\phi \equiv \phi'$ in $F^n(E,\dot{E},y_0)$ and therefore $f \circ \phi \equiv f \circ \phi'$ in $F^n(X,A,x_0)$. Thus the map $f \circ \phi$ defines a unique element $\alpha \in \pi_n(X,A,x_0)$. We shall say that (f,ω,y_0) is a *representative* of α.

Let S be an n-sphere. An *orientation* of S is a generator of $H_n(S)$. Let $y_0 \in S$, let $f:(S,y_0) \to (X,x_0)$ be a map, and let ω be an orientation of S. Then if $\phi,\phi':(I^n,\dot{I}^n) \to (S,y_0)$ are maps such that $\phi_*\omega_n = \phi'_*\omega_n = \omega$, we have $\phi \equiv \phi'$ in $F^n(S,y_0)$ and therefore $f \circ \phi$ and $f \circ \phi'$ define the same element $\alpha \in \pi_n(X,x_0)$. We shall say that (f,ω,y_0) is a *representative* of α.

REMARK. *Let* ω *be an orientation of the n-cell E and let* y_0, $y_1 \in \dot{E}$. *Suppose that* $f:(E,\dot{E}) \to (X,A)$ *is a map. Let p be a path in* $\dot{E}$ *from* y_0 *to* y_1, *and let* $\xi \in \pi_1(A,f(y_0),f(y_1))$ *be the homotopy class of* $f \circ p$. *Then if* α_i *is the element of* $\pi_n(X,A,f(y_i))$ *represented by* $(f,\omega,y_i)(i = 0,1)$, *then* $\alpha_0 = \bar{\theta}(\alpha_1)$. *Similarly for spheres.*

From this we see that if E is an n-cell, ω *an orientation in E, then any map* $f:(E,\dot{E}) \to (X,A)$ *represents a unique element of* $\pi_n^*(X,A)$. *It is further clear that, if f,g are homotopic maps of* $(E,\dot{E})$ *into* (X,A), *they* *define the same element of* $\pi_n^*(X,A)$. *A similar statement holds for maps of spheres.*

NOTE. It is not true in general that two maps of $(E,\dot{E})$ into (X,A) which represent the same element of $\pi_n^*(X,A)$ are homotopic. Similarly for spheres.

2.3 The Eilenberg-Blakers Homology Groups [1, 4]

We present here a sequence of groups, intermediate between the homology and homotopy groups. These were introduced in the absolute case by Eilenberg [4] and in the relative case by Blakers [1].

Let $I^{n,k}$ be the union of the faces of I^n of dimension $\leq k$. If k, l are integers or ∞, let $Q^{k,l}(X,A,x)$ be the subgroup of $Q(X)$ spanned by all singular cubes $f\colon(I^n,I^{n,k},I^{n,l}) \to (X,A,x)$. Factoring by degenerate cubes, we obtain

$$C^{k,l}(X,A,x) = Q^{k,l}(X,A,x)/Q^{k,l}(X,A,x) \cap D(x)$$

Clearly $C^{k,l}(X,A,x)$ is a subcomplex of $C(X)$; we denote its qth homology group with coefficients in G by

$$H_{q;k,l}(X,A,x;G)$$

We also abbreviate $C^{k,-1}(X,x,x)$ to $C^k(X,x)$ and denote its homology groups by $H_{q;k}(X,x;G)$. Evidently

$$\begin{aligned} C^{k,l+1} + C^{k+1,l} &\subset C^{k,l} \\ C^{k,l} &= C^{k,k} \qquad \text{if } l \geq k \\ C^{\infty,-1} &= C(A) \\ C^{-1,-1} &= C(X) \end{aligned}$$

Hereafter we assume for simplicity that X and A are 0-connected.

THEOREM 2.3.1. *If* $\pi_k(X,A,x) = 0$, *then* $(C^{k,l},C^{\infty,l})$ *is chain-equivalent to* $(C^{k-1,l},C^{\infty,l})$.

PROOF. We construct a homomorphism $\Delta\colon Q^{k-1,l} \to Q^{k-1,l}$ such that

1. If f is a singular n-cube, Δf is a singular $(n+1)$-cube.
2. $(\Delta f) \circ \alpha_1^1 \in Q^{k,l}$.
3. $(\Delta f) \circ \alpha_1^0 = f$.
4. $(\Delta f) \circ \alpha_{i+1}^\epsilon = \Delta(f \circ \alpha_i^\epsilon) \qquad (i \geq 1)$.
5. If $f \in Q^{k,l}$, then $\Delta f(t_1,\cdots,t_{n+1}) = f(t_2,\cdots,t_{n+1})$ (i.e., $\Delta f = f \circ \beta_1$).
6. If $f \in D(X)$, then $\Delta f \in D(X)$.

Once this has been done, define $\gamma\colon Q^{k-1,l} \to Q^{k,l}$ by

$$\gamma f = (\Delta f) \circ \alpha_1^1 = \partial\Delta f + \Delta\partial f + f$$

We then have

$$\gamma \text{ is a chain-mapping: } Q^{k-1,l} \to Q^{k,l}$$
$$\gamma | Q^{k,l} = \text{the identity}$$
$$f \in D(X) \Rightarrow \gamma f \in D(X)$$

Hence γ induces $\bar{\gamma}: C^{k-1,l} \to C^{k,l}$, Δ induces $\bar{\Delta}: C^{k-1,l} \to C^{k-1,l}$, and $\bar{\Delta}$ is a chain homotopy of $\bar{\gamma}$ to the identity. Since $C^{\infty,l}, \subset C^{k,l}$, we have $\bar{\gamma}|C^{\infty,l}$ = identity, and therefore $(C^{k,l},C^{\infty,l})$ is chain-equivalent to $(C^{k-1,l},C^{\infty,l})$ as desired.

Construction of Δ. Assume that Δf has been constructed for all cubes $f \in Q^{k-1,l}$ of dimension $\leq q - 1$. Let f be a q cube in $C^{k-1,l}$. If $q \leq k - 1$, then $f \in Q^{k,l}$, and we define Δf by Part 5. Suppose $q \geq k$. If $f \in Q^{k,l}$, define Δf by Part 5. If $f \in D(X)$, we have $f = f \circ \alpha_q^0 \circ \beta_q$; define $\Delta f = \Delta(f \circ \alpha_q^0) \circ \beta_{q+1}$. If $f \in Q^{k,l} \cup D(X)$, we define a map $d: J^q \to X$ as follows: For any $u \in I^q$, $d(0,u) = f(u)$. Now if $u \in \dot{I}^q$, then at least one coordinate, say the ith, must be either 0 or 1, say ϵ. We then define

$$d(t,u) = \Delta(f \circ \alpha_i^\epsilon)(t,\beta_i(u))$$

It is easy to see that these definitions agree on $0 \times \dot{I}^q$.

Now suppose that ϵ_i and ϵ_j, the ith and jth coordinates of u, are 0 or 1. We must check that the two definitions corresponding to the ith and jth coordinates yield the same result. Assume that $i > j$. Then we have

$$\begin{aligned}\Delta(f \circ \alpha_i^{\epsilon_i})(t,\beta_i(u)) &= \Delta(f \circ \alpha_i^{\epsilon_i})(t,\alpha_j^{\epsilon_j}\beta_j\beta_i(u)) \\ &= \Delta(f \circ \alpha_i^{\epsilon_i})(\alpha_{j+1}^{\epsilon_j}(t,\beta_j\beta_i(u))) \\ &= \Delta(f \circ \alpha_i^{\epsilon_i} \circ \alpha_j^{\epsilon_j})(t,\beta_j\beta_i(u))\end{aligned}$$

(by Part 4 and the induction hypothesis)

$$\begin{aligned}&= \Delta(f \circ \alpha_j^{\epsilon_j} \circ \alpha_{i-1}^{\epsilon_i})(t,\beta_{i-1}\beta_j(u)) \\ &= \Delta(f \circ \alpha_j^{\epsilon_j})(t,\beta_j(u))\end{aligned}$$

by reversing the foregoing process. Δ is then well defined.

We may now extend the map Δf from J^q to I^{q+1}. This defines Δf, and it is easily seen that Part 1 and Parts 3 through 6 are satisfied. As for Part 2, this is trivial in case $q > k$, since in that case all k faces are contained in J^q. If $k = q$, Δf may be extended over I^{k+1} in such a way that $\Delta f|1 \times I^k \in A$. This follows from Problem 4, the fact that $\pi_k(X,A,x) = 0$, and the fact that $\Delta f(t,u) = f(u) \in A$ for $u \in \dot{I}^k$. The proof is thus completed.

Corollary 2.3.2. *Under the foregoing hypotheses, the homology sequence of* $(C^{k,l},C^{\infty,l})$ *and* $(C^{k-1,l},C^{\infty,l})$ *are isomorphic. This follows from Theorem* 2.3.1 *and the five-lemma.*

COROLLARY 2.3.3. *If* $\pi_i(X,A,x) = 0$ *for* $1 \leq i \leq k$, *then the homology sequences of* $(C^{k,l},C^{\infty,l})$ *and* $(C^{-1,l},C^{\infty,l})$ *are isomorphic.*

COROLLARY 2.3.4. *If* $\pi_k(X,x) = 0$, *then the complexes* $C^k(X,x)$ *and* $C^{k-1}(X,x)$ *are chain-equivalent.*

COROLLARY 2.3.5. *If* $\pi_i(X,x) = 0$ *for* $0 \leq i \leq k$, *then* $H_q(X) \approx H_q(C^k(X,x))$.

COROLLARY 2.3.6. *If* $\pi_i(X,A,x) = 0$ *for* $1 \leq i \leq k$, *then* $H_q(X,A) \approx H_q(C^{k,0},C^{\infty,0})$.

PROOF. By Corollary 2.3.3, the pairs $(C^{k,0},C^{\infty,0})$ and $(C^{-1,0},C^{\infty,0})$ are chain-equivalent. Now $C^{-1,0}(X,A,x) = C^0(X,x)$ and $C^{\infty,0}(X,A,x) = C^0(A,x)$. But $C^0(X,x)$ and $C^{-1}(X,x) = C(X)$ are chain-equivalent, as are $C^0(A,x)$ and $C^{-1}(A,x) = C(A)$. Hence $(C^{k,0},C^{\infty,0})$ is chain-equivalent with $(C(X),C(A))$.

2.4 The Homotopy Addition Theorem [13]

We now state a lemma which will often be used in the sequel. We are concerned with the following situation. There is given a map $f:I^{n+1} \to X$ which sends every $(n-1)$-dimensional face of I^{n+1} into a subset A of X. Then the map $f \circ \alpha_i^\epsilon:(I^n,\dot{I}^n) \to (X,A)$, with the orientation ω_n on I^n, represents an element $\gamma_i^\epsilon \in \pi_n^*(X,A)$.

THEOREM 2.4.1. (Homotopy addition theorem).

$$\sum_{i=1}^{n+1} \sum_{\epsilon=0}^{1} (-1)^{i+\epsilon}\gamma_i^\epsilon = 0$$

PROOF. Suppose first that $f(\alpha_i^\epsilon(I^n)) \subset A$ for $i > 1$. Then f is a homotopy of $f \circ \alpha_1^0$ to $f \circ \alpha_1^1$ whence $\gamma_1^0 = \gamma_1^1$.

We now prove the theorem by induction on the number m of pairs (i,ϵ) with $i > 1$ such that $f(\alpha_i^\epsilon(I^n)) \not\subset A$. The case $m = 0$ has just been proved. Assuming the result holds for $m \geq 0$, we prove it for $m + 1$. We first need some lemmas.

LEMMA 2.4.2. *Let* $f,g:(I^n,\dot{I}^n) \to (X,A)$ *be maps such that* $f(u,1) = g(u,0)$ *for* $u \in I^{n-1}$. *Let* $h:(I^n,K^{n-1}) \to (X,A)$ *be the map defined by*

$$h(u,t) = \begin{cases} f(u,2t) & (0 \leq t \leq \frac{1}{2}) \\ g(u,2t-1) & (\frac{1}{2} \leq t \leq 1) \end{cases}$$

Let α, β, γ be the elements of $\pi_n^*(X,A)$ represented by f, g, h. Then $\gamma = \alpha + \beta$.

PROOF. Let $y_* = (0,0,\cdots,0,1)$ and let $\Delta_0:(I^n \times I, \dot{I}^n \times I) \rightarrow (I^n,\dot{I}^n)$ be a map such that

$$\begin{cases} \Delta_0(y,0) = y \\ \Delta_0(J^{n-1} \times 1) = y_* \\ \Delta_0(I^{n-1} \times 1 \times I) \subset I^{n-1} \times 1 \end{cases}$$

Let θ be the reflection of I^n about $\{y_n = \frac{1}{2}\}$, and define

$$\Delta_1:(I^n \times I, \dot{I}^n \times I) \rightarrow (I^n,\dot{I}^n)$$

by

$$\Delta_1(y,t) = \theta(\Delta_0(\theta(y),t))$$

Let f_t, g_t be the maps given by

$$\begin{aligned} f_t(y) &= f(\Delta_0(y,t)) \\ g_t(y) &= g(\Delta_1(y,t)) \end{aligned}$$

Then

$$\begin{aligned} g_t(u,0) &= g(\theta(\Delta_0(u,1,t))) \\ &= f(\Delta_0(u,1,t)) \qquad \text{(by *)} \\ &= f_t(u,1) \end{aligned}$$

and therefore we may define

$$h_t(u,s) = \begin{cases} f_t(u,2s) & 0 \leq s \leq \frac{1}{2} \\ g_t(u,2s-1) & \frac{1}{2} \leq s \leq 1 \end{cases}$$

Then f_1, g_1, and h_1 are representatives of α, β, γ. But f_1, g_1, $h_1 \in F^n(X,A,x)$ where $x = f(y_*)$ and $h_1 = f_1 + g_1$. Hence $\gamma = \alpha + \beta$.

NOTE. If f and g satisfy the hypotheses of Lemma 2.4.2, we define $f + g = h$.

LEMMA 2.4.3. *Let $f:(I^n,\dot{I}^n) \rightarrow (X,A)$ be a map. Let $f':(I^n,\dot{I}^n) \rightarrow (X,A)$ be the map defined by*

$$f'(t_1,\cdots,t_n) = f(1 - t_1,t_2,\cdots,t_n)$$

Then if α, α' are the elements of $\pi_n^*(X,A)$ represented by f and f', we have $\alpha' = -\alpha$.

PROOF. Let $g = f + f'$. Then g represents $\alpha + \alpha'$. Also

$$g(t_1,\cdots,t_n) = g(1 - t_1,t_2,\cdots,t_n)$$

Define

$$F(t_1,\cdots,t_n,\lambda) = \begin{cases} g((1-\lambda)t_1,t_2,\cdots,t_n) & 0 \leq t_1 \leq \frac{1}{2} \\ g((1-\lambda)t_1 + \lambda,t_2,\cdots,t_n) & \frac{1}{2} \leq t_1 \leq 1 \end{cases}$$

Then F is a map $(I^n \times I, \dot{I}^n \times I) \rightarrow (X,A)$ and $F(t,0) = g$, $F(t,1) =$

$g(0,t_2,\cdots,t_n) \in A$. Hence g represents the zero element of $\pi_n^*(X,A)$, whence $\alpha + \alpha' = 0$.

LEMMA 2.4.4. *Let π be a permutation of $\{1,\cdots,n\}$ and let $f_\pi:(I^n,\dot{I}^n) \to (I^n,\dot{I}^n)$ be the map such that*

$$f_\pi(t_1,\cdots,t_n) = (t_{\pi(1)},\cdots,t_{\pi(n)})$$

Then $f_{\pi*}\omega_n = (\text{sgn } \pi)\cdot\omega_n$.

PROOF. Define $\phi(\pi) \in Z$ by

$$f_{\pi*}\omega_n = \phi(\pi)\cdot\omega_n$$

Then ϕ is a homomorphism of the symmetric group on n letters into the multiplicative group of $\{1,-1\}$; for

$$\begin{aligned}\phi(\pi \circ \rho)\omega_n &= (f_{\pi \circ \rho})*\omega_n = (f_\pi \circ f_\rho)*\omega_n \\ &= f_{\pi*}f_\rho*\omega_n \\ &= f_\pi*(\phi(\rho)\omega_n) \\ &= \phi(\rho)f_\pi*\omega_n = \phi(\rho)\phi(\pi)\omega_n\end{aligned}$$

and since $1 = \phi(1) = \phi(\pi\pi^{-1}) = \phi(\pi)\phi(\pi^{-1})$, we must have that $\phi(\pi)$ divides 1. If we can show that ϕ is nontrivial, it will follow that $\phi(\pi) = \text{sgn } \pi$.

We therefore prove, by induction on n: if π_n is the transposition (12) on the numbers $(1,\cdots,n)$, then $\phi(\pi_n) = -1$. Suppose $n = 2$. Then

$$f_{\pi_2} \circ \alpha_1^\epsilon = \alpha_2^\epsilon, \qquad f_{\pi_2} \circ \alpha_2^\epsilon = \alpha_1^\epsilon$$

and therefore

$$\begin{aligned}\partial f_{\pi_2} &= f_{\pi_2} \circ \alpha_1^1 - f_{\pi_2} \circ \alpha_1^0 - f_{\pi_2} \circ \alpha_2^1 + f_{\pi_2} \circ \alpha_2^0 \\ &= \alpha_2^1 - \alpha_2^0 - \alpha_1^1 + \alpha_1^0 \\ &= -\partial i\end{aligned}$$

where i is the identity map of I^2. Hence

$$\begin{aligned}\partial * f_{\pi_2*}\omega_2 &= [\partial f_{\pi_2}] + B_1(I_2) \\ &= -[\partial i] + B_1(I_2) \\ &= -\partial_* i_* \omega_2 = -\partial_*\omega_2\end{aligned}$$

But $\partial_*:H_2(I^2,\dot{I}^2) \approx H_1(\dot{I}^2)$, whence $f_{\pi_2*}\omega_2 = -\omega_2$.

Now suppose the assertion holds for $n-1$, $n \geq 3$. Let

$$\psi:H_{n-1}(I^{n-1},\dot{I}^{n-1}) \approx H_n(I^n,\dot{I}^n)$$

be the canonical mapping (see the proof of Lemma 2.1.1(b)). Then $f_{\pi_n*}\psi = \psi f_{\pi_{n-1}*}$. To prove this, it is sufficient to prove that it is true when ψ is replaced by any of its component mappings. For ∂_*, this is a consequence of the third Eilenberg-Steenrod axiom [B.3, p. 11]. For e_* and j_* it is trivial; for α^1_{n*} it follows from

$$\begin{aligned} f_{\pi_n}\alpha_n^1(t_1,\cdots,t_{n-1}) &= f_{\pi_n}(t_1,\cdots,t_{n-1},1) \\ &= (t_2,t_1,t_3,\cdots,t_{n-1},1) \\ &= \alpha_n^1(t_2,t_3,\cdots,t_{n-1}) \\ &= \alpha_n^1 f_{\pi_{n-1}}(t_1,\cdots,t_{n-1}) \end{aligned}$$

Therefore we have

$$\begin{aligned} f_{\pi_n*}(\omega_n) &= f_{\pi_n*}(\psi(\omega_{n-1})) = \psi(f_{\pi_{n-1}*}(\omega_{n-1})) \\ &= \psi(-\omega_{n-1}) = -\psi(\omega_{n-1}) = -\omega_n \end{aligned}$$ Q.E.D

For each (i,ϵ) with $i > 1$, let $J_i^\epsilon = I_{i,\epsilon}^n \cup I_{1,1}^n$. Define a map $\phi_i^\epsilon: I^n \to J_i^\epsilon$ by

$$\phi_i^\epsilon(t_1,\cdots,t_n) = \begin{cases} (2t_{i-1},t_1,\cdots,t_{i-2},0,t_i,\cdots,t_n) & 0 \leq t_{i-1} \leq \frac{1}{2} \\ (1,t_1,\cdots,t_{i-2},2t_{i-1}-1,t_i,\cdots,t_n) & \frac{1}{2} \leq t_{i-1} \leq 1 \end{cases} \quad \text{if } \epsilon = 0$$

$$\phi_i(t_1,\cdots,t_n) = \begin{cases} (1,t_1,\cdots,t_{i-2},2t_{i-1},t_i,\cdots,t_n) & 0 \leq t_{i-1} \leq \frac{1}{2} \\ (2-2t_{i-1},t_1,\cdots,t_{i-2},1,t_i,\cdots,t_n) & \frac{1}{2} \leq t_{i-1} \leq 1 \end{cases} \quad \text{if } \epsilon = 1$$

LEMMA 2.4.5. *The map* $f \circ \phi_i^\epsilon:(I^n,\dot I^n) \to (X,A)$ *represents the element* $\gamma_1^1 + (-1)^{i+\epsilon}\gamma_i^\epsilon \in \pi_n^*(X,A)$.

PROOF. Let π be the permutation $(1,2,\cdots,i-1)$ of $\{1,\cdots,n\}$, and let f_π be the map of Lemma 2.4.4. Then

$$f \circ \phi_i^\epsilon = \begin{cases} f \circ \alpha_i^0 \circ f_\pi + f \circ \alpha_1^1 & \text{if } \epsilon = 0 \\ f \circ \alpha_1^1 - f \circ \alpha_i^1 \circ f_\pi & \text{if } \epsilon = 1 \end{cases}$$

Since f_π has degree sgn $\pi = (-1)^i$ by Lemma 2.4.4, we see that $f \circ \phi_i$ represents

$$\begin{aligned} &(-1)^i\gamma_i^0 + \gamma_1^1 && \text{if } \epsilon = 0 \\ &\gamma_1^1 - (-1)^i\gamma_i^1 && \text{if } \epsilon = 1 \end{aligned}$$

Since $\pi_n^*(X,A)$ is abelian, the conclusion follows.

LEMMA 2.4.6. *For each* (i,ϵ), *there is a map* $\phi:I^{n+1} \times I \to X$ *such that*

1. $\phi(u,0) = f(u)$.
2. $\phi(u,\lambda) \in A$ *if* $u \in \dot I_{j,\eta}^n$ *and* $(1,1) \neq (j,\eta) \neq (i,\epsilon)$.
3. $\phi(u,1) \in A$ *if* $u \in I_{i,\epsilon}^n$.
4. $\phi(u,\lambda) \in A$ *if* $u \in I_{j,\eta}^n$ *and* $f(I_{j,\eta}^n) \subset A$.
5. $\phi(\alpha_1^1(u),1) = f(\phi_i^\epsilon(u))$ *if* $u \in I^{n-1}$.

PROOF. We first define a map ψ on $I_{1,1}^n \times I$ as follows:

If $\epsilon = 1$,

$\psi(\alpha_1^1(t),\lambda)$

$$= \begin{cases} f(1,t_1,\cdots,t_{i-2}, \\ \quad (1+2\lambda)t_{i-1},t_i,\cdots,t_n) & 0 \le t_{i-1} \le \frac{1}{2} \\ f(1,t_1,\cdots,t_{i-2}, \\ \quad (1-2\lambda)t_{i-1}+2\lambda,t_i,\cdots,t_n) & \frac{1}{2} \le t_{i-1} \le 1 \end{cases} \Bigg\} \; 0 \le \lambda \le \tfrac{1}{2}$$

$$\begin{cases} f(1,t_1,\cdots,t_{i-2},2t_{i-1},t_i,\cdots,t_n) & 0 \le t_{i-1} \le \frac{1}{2} \\ f(2(1-\lambda)+2(2\lambda-1)(1-t_{i-1}), \\ \quad t_1,\cdots,t_{i-2},1,t_i,\cdots,t_n) & \frac{1}{2} \le t_{i-1} \le 1 \end{cases} \Bigg\} \; \tfrac{1}{2} \le \lambda \le 1$$

If $\epsilon = 0$,

$\psi(\alpha_1^1(t),\lambda)$

$$= \begin{cases} f(1,t_1,\cdots,t_{i-2}, \\ \quad (1-2\lambda)t_{i-1},t_i,\cdots,t_n) & 0 \le t_{i-1} \le \frac{1}{2} \\ f(1,t_1,\cdots,t_{i-2} \\ \quad (1+2\lambda)t_{i-1}-2\lambda,t_i,\cdots,t_n) & \frac{1}{2} \le t_{i-1} \le 1 \end{cases} \Bigg\} \; 0 \le \lambda \le \tfrac{1}{2}$$

$$\begin{cases} f(2(1-\lambda)+2(2\lambda-1)t_{i-1}, \\ \quad t_1,\cdots,t_{i-2},0,t_i,\cdots,t_n) & 0 \le t_{i-1} \le \frac{1}{2} \\ f(1,t_i,\cdots,t_{i-2},2t_{i-1}-1,t_i,\cdots,t_n) & \frac{1}{2} \le t_{i-1} \le 1 \end{cases} \Bigg\} \; \tfrac{1}{2} \le \lambda \le 1$$

Now define ψ on $I_{i,\epsilon}^n \times I$ by

$$\psi(\alpha_i^\epsilon(t),\lambda) = \begin{cases} f(\alpha_i^\epsilon(t)) & 0 \le \lambda \le \frac{1}{2} \\ f(2(1-\lambda)t_1,t_2,\cdots,t_{i-1},\epsilon,t_i,\cdots,t_n) & \frac{1}{2} \le \lambda \le 1 \end{cases}$$

We have thus defined a map $\phi: J_i^\epsilon \times I \to X$.

Now let $K = I^{n+1}$, $L =$ the union of $I^{n+1,n-1}$ with those n-dimensional faces $I_{i,\epsilon}^n$ with $i > 1$ for which $f(I_{i,\epsilon}^n) \subset A$, $K_0 = J_i^\epsilon$. Then $L_0 = K_0 \cap L = \dot{J}_i^\epsilon$. Now $\psi:(K_0 \times I, L_0 \times I) \to (X,A)$. By Corollary 1.2, ψ has an extension $\phi:(K \times I, L \times I) \to (X,A)$ with $\phi(x,0) = f(x)$.

We can now complete the proof of the theorem. Let f be a map such that, for $(m+1)$ pairs (i,ϵ) with $i > 1$, $f(I_{i,\epsilon}^n) \not\subset A$. Choose one such pair (i,ϵ). Let ϕ be a map as in Lemma 2.4.6, and define $f': I^{n+1} \to A$ by $f'(t) = \phi(t,1)$. Then f' satisfies the hypotheses of the theorem and f' fails to carry only m of the faces $I_{i,\epsilon}^n$ $(i > 1)$ into A. Hence we may apply the induction hypothesis to f'. Let $\bar{\gamma}_j^\eta$ be the element represented by $f' \circ \alpha_j^\eta$. It is then clear that

$$\bar{\gamma}_j^\eta = \gamma_j^\eta \qquad \text{unless } (j,\eta) = (1,1) \text{ or } (i,\epsilon)$$
$$\bar{\gamma}_i^\epsilon = 0$$

By Lemma 4.5, $\bar{\gamma}_1^1 = \gamma_1^1 + (-1)^{i+\epsilon}\gamma_i^\epsilon$. But

$$0 = \sum (-1)^{j+\eta}\bar{\gamma}_j^\eta = \sum (-1)^{j+\eta}\gamma_j^\eta$$

and the proof is complete.

REMARK. *We have assumed here $n \geq 2$, since $\pi_1(X,A)$ is not a group. However, if $n = 1$ and A is a single point, our result still holds if $\pi_1^*(X,A)$ is replaced by $\pi_1^*(X)$ and is much simpler to prove.*

2.5 The Hurewicz Theorem [1, 12]

THEOREM 2.5.1. *Let X be a space, A a subspace, $x \in A$. Then, if $n > 1$,*

$$H_n(C^{n-1,0}(X,A,x),C^{\infty,0}(X,A,x)) \approx \pi_n^*(X,A)$$

If A is a single point x and $n = 1$, then

$$H_n(C^0(X,x),C^\infty(X,x)) \approx \pi_n^*(X)$$

PROOF. Let $f = (I^n,\dot{I}^n,J^{n-1}) \to (X,A,x)$ be a map. Then f is an n-cell of $Q^{n-1,0}(X,A,x)$ and therefore a relative cycle of $Q^{n-1,0}$ modulo $Q^{\infty,0}$. If F is a free homotopy of f in $G^n(X,A)$ via a path p, then F is an $(n+1)$ cube in $Q^{n-1,0}$ and

$$\partial F = g - f + \sum_{\substack{i>1 \\ \epsilon}} (-1)^{i+\epsilon} F \circ \alpha_i^\epsilon$$

Each $F \circ \alpha_i^\epsilon$ with $i > 1$ is an n-cube in A and therefore belongs to $Q^{\infty,0}$. Hence $f \sim g \bmod Q^{\infty,0}$. Therefore we have a natural map $\bar{\rho}:\pi_n^*(X,A) \to H_n(C^{n-1,0},C^{\infty,0})$. Evidently, $\rho = i_* \circ \bar{\rho}$, where i_* is the homomorphism of $H_n(C^{n-1,0},C^{\infty,0})$ into $H_n(X,A)$ induced by the inclusion map. The proof that $\bar{\rho}$ is a homomorphism is essentially the same as the proof that ρ is a homomorphism.

Now define $\sigma: Q^{n-1,0} \to \pi_n^*(X,A)$ by: σf is the element of $\pi_n^*(X,A)$ represented by f for any n-cube $f \in Q^{n-1,0}$. If f is degenerate, then $f(I^n) \subset A$, whence $\sigma f = 0$. If f is an $(n+1)$-cube in $Q^{n-1,0}$, then by the homotopy addition theorem $\sigma(\partial f) = \sum (-1)^{i+\epsilon}\gamma_i^\epsilon = 0$. If f is an n-cube in $C^{\infty,0}$, then $f(I^n) \subset A$ and therefore $\sigma f = 0$. Hence

$$\sigma:(Z_n(C^{n-1,0},C^{\infty,0}),B_n(C^{n-1,0},B^{\infty,0})) \to (\pi_n^*(X,A),0)$$

and therefore σ induces $\sigma_*: H_n(C^{n-1,0},C^{\infty,0}) \to \pi_n^*(X,A)$. Now clearly $\bar{\rho} \circ \sigma_* =$ identity, $\sigma_* \circ \bar{\rho} =$ identity, whence $\bar{\rho}$ is an isomorphism onto and σ_* is its inverse.

The proof of the second statement is the same except for terminology.

As a corollary, we obtain the Hurewicz theorems.

THEOREM 2.5.2. *If (X,A) is $(n-1)$-connected, then*

$$\rho:\pi_n^*(X,A) \approx H_n(X,A)$$

THEOREM 2.5.3. *If X is $(n-1)$-connected, then*

$$\begin{cases} \bar{\rho}:\pi_n(X) \approx H_n(X) & \text{if } n > 1 \\ \bar{\rho}:\pi_n^*(X) \approx H_n(x) & \text{if } n = 1 \end{cases}$$

COROLLARY 2.5.4. *If (X,A) is $(n-1)$-connected and A is 1-connected, then*

$$\rho:\pi_n(X,A) \approx H_n(X,A)$$

PROOF. Since $\pi_1(A) = 0$, we have $\xi = 0$ for $\xi \in \pi_1(A)$; therefore $\bar{\theta}_\xi(\alpha) = \alpha$ for $\alpha \in \pi_n(X,A)$; therefore $\bar{\Omega}_n(X,A) = 0$ and $\pi_n^*(X,A) = \pi_n(X,A)$.

2.6 CW Complexes [26]

DEFINITION. *Let X be a Hausdorff space, Y a closed subspace of X, and $\{J_n\}$ a family of indexing sets. A* CW *decomposition of (X,Y) is a collection $\{E_\alpha^n | n = 0,1,2,\cdots; \alpha \in J_n\}$ of closed subsets of X satisfying the following conditions. Let*

$$X^n = Y \cup \bigcup_{m \leq n} \bigcup_{\alpha \in J_m} E_\alpha^m, \qquad E_\alpha^n = \dot{E}_\alpha^n \cap X^{n-1}\cdot \text{Int } E_\alpha^n = E_\alpha^n - E_\alpha^n$$

Then:

1. *The sets* Int E_α^n *are mutually disjoint, and*

$$X - Y = \bigcup_{n,\alpha} \text{Int } E_\alpha^n$$

2. *There are maps $f_\alpha^n:(I^n,\dot{I}^n) \to (E_\alpha^n,\dot{E}_\alpha^n)$ such that $f_\alpha^n(I^n) = E_\alpha^n$ and f_α^n maps* Int I^n *homeomorphically onto* Int E_α^n.
3. *$\dot{E}_\alpha^n$ meets only a finite number of the sets* Int E_β^q.
4. *A subset A of X is closed if and only if each of the sets $A \cap E_\alpha^n$ and $A \cap Y$ are closed.*

Under these circumstances we say that (X,Y) is a *relative* CW *complex.* The sets E_α^n are called the n-cells of (X,Y), and the map f_α^n is called a *characteristic map* for the n-cell E_α^n.

A relative CW complex (X_1,Y_1) is said to be a *subcomplex* of (X,Y) if and only if X_1 is a subspace of X, Y_1 is a closed subset of Y, and each cell of (X_1,Y_1) is a cell of (X,Y).

This notion of complex is a generalization of that given by J. H. C. Whitehead [26]. The generalization consists of "relativising" the notion of complex; i.e., J. H. C. Whitehead's differs from ours in the sense that he takes $Y = \phi$.

EXAMPLES. 1. If K is a simplicial complex, then $|K|$ is a CW complex.
2. If X is a CW complex and Y a subcomplex, then (X,Y) is a relative CW complex.

3. If (X,Y) is a relative CW complex, then (X^n,Y) is a subcomplex of (X,Y).

PROBLEM 6. If (X,Y) is a relative CW complex and C is a countably compact subset of X, then there is a finite subcomplex (X_1,Y_1) of (X,Y) such that $C \subset X_1$.

PROBLEM 7. If (X,Y) is a relative CW complex, then $(X \times I,\ Y \times I)$ is a CW complex with cells $E^p_\alpha \times 0$, $E^p_\alpha \times 1$, $E^p_\alpha \times I$.

REMARK 2.6.1. *Each cell of (X,Y) is contained in a finite subcomplex (X_1,Y) (i.e., the number of cells in (X_1,Y) is finite).*

PROOF. Let E^n_α be an n-cell, and define sets $A_n, \cdots, A_0$ inductively by

* $A_n = E^n_\alpha$

** A_{i-1} is the union of the cells of dimension $\leq i-1$ of (X,Y) whose interiors meet A_i.

Let $X_1 = Y \cup A_0 \cup \cdots \cup A_n$; we make (X_1,Y) into a relative CW complex by taking as the cells of (X_1,Y) those cells E^p_β of (X,Y) such that $E^p_\beta \subset X_1$. It is enough to prove that Int_{X_1}, i.e., Int taken in the sense of the complex X_1, in the same as Int_X. For then Definitions 1, 2, and 3 are automatic; from Definition 3, *, and ** it follows that X_1 is a finite complex; from this and Definition 2 it follows that X_1 is compact, and thence closed; and then the truth of Definition 4 for X_1 is easily deduced from the truth of Definition 4 for X.

Now clearly $\mathrm{Int}_{X_1} \subset \mathrm{Int}_X$, since $X_1^m \subset X^m$; as for the opposite inequality, let $x \in \mathrm{Int}_{X_1} E^p_\beta \subset A_i$, so that

$$*** \qquad x \notin Y \cup \bigcup_{m \leq p-1} \bigcup_{\alpha \in J'_m} E^m_\alpha$$

where

$$J'_m = \{\alpha | E^m_\alpha \subset X_1\}$$

If $x \notin \mathrm{Int}_X E^p_\beta$, then

$$x \in \dot{E}^p_\beta \subset \bigcup_{m \leq p-1} \bigcup_{\alpha \in J_m} E^m_\alpha$$

By Definition 1, it must be in the Int_X of one of these, say E^q_γ, with $q \leq p-1$. But from ** it then follows that $E^q_\gamma \subset A_{i-1} \subset X_1$; so $\gamma \in J'_q$, contrary to ***. It follows that $x \in \mathrm{Int}_X E^p_\beta$; so $\mathrm{Int}_{X_1} \subset \mathrm{Int}_X$. This completes the proof.

REMARK 2.6.2. *If (X_1,Y_1) is a subcomplex of (X,Y), then X_1 is closed.*

PROOF. If E^n_α is any cell of (X, Y), then

$$X_1 \cap E^n_\alpha = E^n_\alpha \cap (Y_1 \cup \bigcup_p \bigcup_{\beta \in J'_p} \text{Int } E^p_\beta)$$

Let $J = \{(\beta, p) | \beta \in J'_p \text{ and } E^n_\alpha \cap \text{Int } E^p_\beta \neq \phi\}$; J is finite. Now we claim

$$X_1 \cap E^n_\alpha = (Y \cap E^n_\alpha) \cup \bigcup_{(\beta,p) \in J} (E^p_\beta \cap E^n_\alpha)$$

In fact,

$$X_1 \cap E^n_\alpha = E^n_\alpha \cap (Y_1 \cup \bigcup_{(\beta,p) \in J} \text{Int } E^p_\beta) \subset (E^n_\alpha \cap Y_1) \cup \bigcup_{(\beta,p) \in J} (E^n_\alpha \cap E^p_\beta)$$

Conversely, if $(\beta,p) \in J$, then $E^p_\beta \subset X_1$, and therefore $E^p_\beta \cap E^n_\alpha \subset X_1 \cap E^n_\alpha$. Hence the opposite inclusion holds. The result now follows from Definition 4. As a corollary, we have that $Y_1 = X_1 \cap Y$ is closed.

LEMMA 2.6.3. *$\dot{E}^q_\alpha$ is a neighborhood deformation retract of E^q_α, and if f^q_α is a characteristic map, then*

$$(f^q_\alpha)_*: H_p(I^q, \dot{I}^q) \approx H_p(E^q_\alpha, \dot{E}^q_\alpha)$$

for all p.

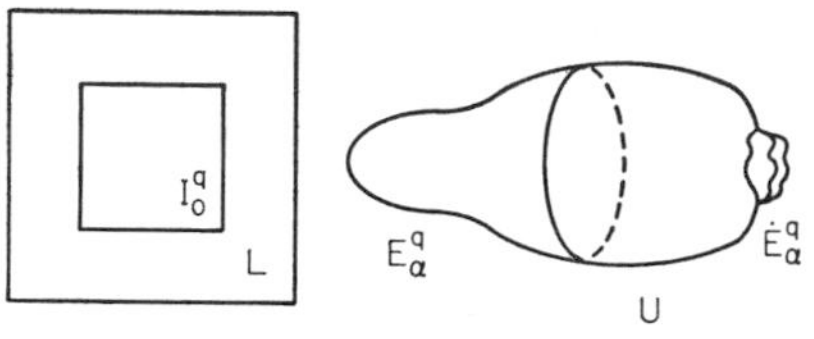

PROOF. Let I^q_0 be a cube $\subset$ Int I^q, and let $L^q = I^q - I^q_0$. Then $\dot{I}^q$ is a deformation retract of L^q; let $\phi: L^q \times I \to L^q$ be a map such that

$$\begin{cases} \phi(u,0) = u \\ \phi(u,1) \in \dot{I}^q \\ \phi(u,t) = u \qquad \text{if } u \in \dot{I}^q \end{cases}$$

Let $U = f^q_\alpha(L^q)$; since I^q is compact, E^q_α is an identification space of I^q under f^q_α. Since $(f^q_\alpha)^{-1}U = L^q$, U is open in E^q_α. Now define $\psi: U \times I \to U$ by

$$\psi(x,t) = f^q_\alpha(\phi((f^q_\alpha)^{-1}(x),t))$$

Since E^q_α is an identification space and ψ is well defined, it is continuous. Evidently

$$\begin{aligned} \psi(x,0) &= x \\ \psi(x,1) &\in \dot{E}^q_\alpha \\ \psi(x,t) &= x \qquad \text{if } x \in \dot{E}^q_\alpha \end{aligned}$$

This proves the first statement.

Now consider the commutative diagram

$$
\begin{array}{ccccc}
H_p(I^q,\dot{I}^q) & \xrightarrow{f_4} & H_p(I^q,L^q) & \xleftarrow{f_5} & H_p(\text{Int } I^q, \text{Int } I^q \cap L^q) \\
\downarrow f_1 & & \downarrow f_2 & & \downarrow f_3 \\
H_p(E^q_\alpha,\dot{E}^q_\alpha) & \xrightarrow{f_6} & H_p(E^q_\alpha,U) & \xleftarrow{f_7} & H_p(\text{Int } E^q_\alpha, \text{Int } E^q_\alpha \cap U)
\end{array}
$$

in which the horizontal homomorphisms are induced by inclusion maps and the vertical ones by f^q_α.

f_3 is an isomorphism onto since $f^q_\alpha|\text{Int } I^q$ is a homeomorphism.

f_5 and f_7 are excisions and therefore isomorphisms onto. Hence

f_2 is an isomorphism onto. But f_4 and f_6 are isomorphisms onto since $\dot{I}^q$ and $\dot{E}^q_\alpha$ are deformation retracts of L^q, U. Hence f_1 is an isomorphism onto. Q.E.D.

COROLLARY 2.6.4. *X^{p-1} is a neighborhood deformation retract of $E^p_\alpha \cup X^{p-1}$, and the inclusion map induces isomorphisms onto:*

$$H_q(E^p_\alpha,\dot{E}^p_\alpha) \approx H_q(E^p_\alpha \cup X^{p-1},X^{p-1})$$

PROOF. Excision.

LEMMA 2.6.5. *Let (X,Y) be a relative* CW *complex, C compact $\subset X$. Then C meets only finitely many interiors of cells of (X,Y).*

PROOF. Let C' be a set of points obtained by choosing one point of C in each interior which C meets. Let B be an arbitrary subset of C'. By 1 and 3 of the definition of a CW complex, each cell of (X,Y) intersects B in a finite set. It then follows from Definition 4 that B is closed. It is therefore closed in C' as well. It follows that every subset of C' is closed, so that the topology induced on C' by the topology of X is trivial; hence if C' were infinite, it could not be compact. On the other hand, C' is itself closed and so is closed in C, which is compact. So C' must be compact. Q.E.D.

COROLLARY 2.6.6. *Let (X,Y) be a relative* CW *complex, C compact $\subset X$. Then there exists a finite subcomplex (X_0,Y) of (X,Y) with $C \subset X_0$.*

PROOF. Proved like Remark 2.6.1. We take as the starting set the set $\bigcup_i E^{n_i}_{\alpha_i}$, where the $E^{n_i}_{\alpha_i}$ are the cells whose interiors are met by C.

Q.E.D.

Let (X,Y) be a relative CW complex. We define a chain complex $C(X,Y)$ by

$$C_p(X,Y) = H_p(X^p,X^{p-1})$$

$\partial: C_p(X,Y) \to C_{p-1}(X,Y)$ is the boundary homomorphism of the homology sequence of the triple (X^p,X^{p-1},X^{p-2}).

For each p-cell E^p_α of X, choose a characteristic map f^p_α and let $e^p_\alpha = (f^p_\alpha)_*(\omega_p) \in H_p(X^p, X^{p-1})$.

THEOREM 2.6.7. *$C_p(X,Y)$ is a free abelian group with the e^p_α as basis. If $q \neq p$, then $H_q(X^p,X^{p-1}) = 0$.*

PROOF. If (X,Y) is finite, the proof is essentially the same as that of Eilenberg-Steenrod for simplicial complexes. In the general case, let $c \in Z_q(X^p,X^{p-1})$. Then $|c|$ is compact and therefore there is a finite subcomplex (X_0, Y) of (X,Y) such that $|c| \subset X_0$. Then $c \in Z_q(X^p_0,X^{p-1}_0)$. If $q \neq p$, since $H_q(X^p,X^{p-1}) = 0$, we have $c = \partial a + b$ with $a \in C_{q+1}(X^p_0)$ and $b \in C_q(X^{p-1}_0)$. Then $a \in C_{q+1}(X^p)$, $b \in C_q(X^{p-1})$ and therefore $c \in B_q(X^p,X^{p-1})$. If $q = p$, we have, by the truth of the theorem for (X_0, Y),

$$c = \partial a + b + \sum_\alpha \gamma_\alpha f^p_\alpha$$

where $a \in C_{p+1}(X^p_0)$, $b \in C_p(X^{p-1}_0)$, and the γ_α are integers such that $\gamma_\alpha = 0$ if $E^p_\alpha \not\subset X_0$. Hence $c \sim \sum \gamma_\alpha f^p_\alpha$ in X^p mod X^{p-1}, and therefore the e^p_α generate $C_p(X,Y)$. Finally suppose $\sum \gamma_\alpha e^p_\alpha = 0$ (γ_α integers, almost all 0); then

$$\sum \gamma_\alpha f^p_\alpha = \partial a + b$$

with $a \in C_{p+1}(X^p)$, $b \in C_p(X^{p-1})$. Then $C = \bigcup_\alpha |\gamma_\alpha f^p_\alpha| \cup |a| \cup |b|$ is compact, and therefore $C \subset X_0$ for some finite subcomplex (X_0, Y) of (X,Y). Then $a \in C_{p+1}(X^p_0)$, $b \in C_p(X^{p-1}_0)$, and therefore $\sum \gamma_\alpha f^p_\alpha \sim 0$ in X^p_0 mod X^{p-1}_0. Hence all the $\gamma_\alpha = 0$, and the e^p_α are linearly independent. Q.E.D.

COROLLARY 2.6.8. $H_q(X^p, Y) = 0$ *if* $q > p$.

PROOF. By induction on p. If $p = -1$, $X^p = Y$, and the statement is true. Suppose that $H_q(X^{p-1},Y) = 0$ and $q > p$. Then the sequence

$$H_{q+1}(X^p,X^{p-1}) \to H_q(X^{p-1},Y) \to H_q(X^p,Y) \to H_q(X^p,X^{p-1})$$

is exact, and the two end groups are zero by Theorem 2.6.7. Hence $H_q(X^p,Y) \approx H_q(X^{p-1},Y) = 0$.

COROLLARY 2.6.9. *$H_q(X^p,Y) \approx H_q(X,Y)$ under the inclusion map if $q < p$.*

PROOF. We first show that $H_q(X^p,Y) \approx H_q(X^{p+1},Y)$ under inclusion. The sequence

$$H_{q+1}(X^{p+1},X^p) \to H_q(X^p,Y) \to H_q(X^{p+1},Y) \to H_q(X^{p+1},X^p)$$

is exact, and the end groups are zero. Hence the intermediate groups are isomorphic, as desired.

Now let c be a relative q-cycle of $X^p \bmod Y$ $(q < p)$ and suppose $c \sim 0$ in $X \bmod Y$. Then $c = \partial a + b$ with $a \in C_{q+1}(X)$, $b \in C_q(Y)$. Then $|c| \cup |a| \cup |b|$ is contained in X_0 for some finite subcomplex (X_0, Y) and therefore in X^r for some $r \geq p$. Thus $c \sim 0$ in $X^r \bmod Y$. But $H_q(X^p, Y) \approx H_q(X^r, Y)$, whence $c \sim 0$ in $X^p \bmod Y$. Hence the homomorphism $H_q(X^p, Y) \to H_q(X, Y)$ is an isomorphism into.

Finally, let c be a relative q-cycle of (X, Y). Then $|c| \subset X^r$ for some r. If $r \leq p$, then $|c| \subset X^p$, and therefore c is a relative cycle of $X^p \bmod Y$. If $r > p$, then $H_q(X^p, Y) \approx H_q(X^r, Y)$, and therefore c is homologous mod Y to a relative cycle of $X^p \bmod Y$. Hence the homomorphism $H_q(X^p, Y) \to H_q(X, Y)$ is onto.

THEOREM 2.6.10. *The homology groups of the chain complex $C(X, Y)$ are isomorphic with those of (X, Y).*

PROOF. Consider the diagram

$$
\begin{array}{ccccccccc}
 & & H_p(X^{p-1}, Y) & & & & H_{p-1}(X^{p-2}, Y) & & \\
 & & \downarrow{\scriptstyle j_1} & & & & \downarrow{\scriptstyle j_2} & & \\
H_{p+1}(X^{p+1}, X^p) & \longrightarrow & H_p(X^p, Y) & \xrightarrow{i_1} & H_p(X^p, X^{p-1}) & \xrightarrow{\partial_2} & H_{p-1}(X^{p-1}, Y) & \xrightarrow{i_2} & H_{p-1}(X^{p-1}, X^{p-2}) \\
 & & \downarrow{\scriptstyle i_3} & & & & & & \\
 & & H_p(X^{p+1}, Y) & \xrightarrow{i_4} & H_p(X^{p+1}, X^p) & & & &
\end{array}
$$

Evidently $i_1 \circ \partial_1 = \partial : C_{p+1}(X, Y) \to C_p(X, Y)$ and $i_2 \circ \partial_2 = \partial : C_p(X, Y) \to C_{p-1}(X, Y)$. Now by Corollary 2.6.8, $H_{p-1}(X^{p-2}, Y) = 0$, whence i_2 is an isomorphism into. Hence $Z_p(C(X, Y)) = \text{Kernel } i_2 \circ \partial_2 = \text{Kernel } \partial_2 = \text{Image } i_1$. Also $H_p(X^{p-1}, Y) = 0$ by Corollary 2.6.8, whence i_1 is an isomorphism into. Now $B_p(C(X, Y)) = \text{Image } (i_1 \circ \partial_1) = i_1(\text{Image } \partial_1)$. Since i_1 is an isomorphism of $H_p(X^p, Y)$ onto Image i_1, we see that

$$
\begin{aligned}
H_p(C(X, Y)) = \frac{Z_p(C(X, Y))}{B_p(C(X, Y))} &\approx \frac{H_p(X^p, Y)}{\text{Image } \partial_1} \\
&= \frac{H_p(X^p, Y)}{\text{Kernel } i_3} \\
&\approx \text{Image } i_3
\end{aligned}
$$

But $H_p(X^{p+1}, X^p) = 0$, whence i_3 is onto, so that

$$
\begin{aligned}
H_p(C(X, Y)) &\approx H_p(X^{p+1}, Y) \\
&\approx H_p(X, Y) \qquad \text{by Corollary 2.6.9}
\end{aligned}
$$

Q.E.D.

REMARK. *It follows from the universal coefficient theorem that Corollaries* 2.6.8 *and* 2.6.9 *and Theorem* 2.6.10 *hold for homology and cohomology groups with any coefficient group.*

PROBLEM 8. We may regard I^n as a CW complex with n-cell I^n, $(n-1)$-cells $I^{n-1}_{i,\epsilon}$, etc. Let α_i^ϵ be the characteristic map for $I^{n-1}_{i,\epsilon}$, and let the identity be the characteristic map for I^n. Then, if $e^{n-1}_{i,\epsilon}$ and e^n are the chains determined by these characteristic maps, we have

$$\partial e^n = \sum_{i,\epsilon} (-1)^{i+\epsilon} e^{n-1}_{i,\epsilon}$$

PROBLEM 9. Let (X,Y) be a relative CW complex. Then X is connected if and only if X^1 is connected.

THEOREM 2.6.11. *Let* (X,Y) *be a relative* CW *complex,* W *a space,* $\phi: Y \to W$ *a map. Suppose that* W *is* $(n-1)$*-connected. Then* ϕ *has an extension* $\bar{\phi}: X^n \to W$.

PROOF. Let E^0_α be a 0-cell of X. Then E^0_α is a point of $X - Y$, and we define $\phi_0: X^0 \to W$ by

$$\phi_0 | Y = f, \ \phi_0(E^0_\alpha) = w_0$$

where w_0 is a point of W.

Suppose that we have found an extension $\phi_p: X^p \to W$ of ϕ with $p < n$. Let f^{p+1}_α be a characteristic map for the cell E^{p+1}_α. Then $\phi_p \circ f^{p+1}_\alpha | \dot{I}^{p+1}: \dot{I}^{p+1} \to W$. Since W is $(n-1)$-connected, this map has an extension $g: I^{p+1} \to W$. Define $\phi^\alpha_{p+1}: E^{p+1}_\alpha \to W$ by $\phi^\alpha_{p+1} = g \circ (f^{p+1}_\alpha)^{-1}$. Then define $\phi_{p+1}: X^{p+1} \to W$ by

$$\begin{cases} \phi_{p+1} | X^p = \phi_p \\ \phi_{p+1} | E^{p+1}_\alpha = \phi^\alpha_{p+1} \end{cases}$$

Then ϕ_{p+1} is well defined and continuous on each cell and on Y. Hence it is continuous.

LEMMA 2.6.12. *Let* (X,Y) *be a relative* CW *complex with precisely one* n*-cell* E^n *and none of higher degree. Then* (X,X^{n-1}) *is* $(n-1)$*-connected.*

PROOF. Let $\phi: (I^p,\dot{I}^p) \to (X,X^{n-1})$ be a map with $p \leq n-1$. We must show that ϕ is homotopic relative to $\dot{I}^p$ to a map h^n which takes I^p into X^{n-1}. Let $s_1 = (\frac{1}{2},\cdots,\frac{1}{2}) \in I^n$, f a characteristic map for E^n, $x = f(s_1) \in \text{Int } E^n$, $Q = \phi^{-1}(x)$.

Let I^n_1 and I^n_2 be two copies of the n-cube with $u \in \text{Int } I^n_1 \subset I^n_1 \subset \text{Int } I^n_2 \subset I^n_2 \subset \text{Int } I^n$, $U = f(I^n - I^n_1)$, $V = f(\text{Int } I^n_2)$. Then U and V are sets open in E^n which cover E^n. Choose a simplicial decomposition (K,L) of $(I^p,\dot{I}^p)$ so that each simplex of K is contained in either U or V, and let T be the union of those simplexes of K which meet Q; then T is a neighborhood of Q in I^p. If σ is a simplex of T, then $\phi(\sigma)$ contains $x \notin U$, and therefore $\phi(\sigma) \subset V$. Hence

$$f^{-1} \circ \phi|\dot{T}: \qquad \dot{T} \to \operatorname{Int} I_2^n - \{u\}$$

But $\operatorname{Int} I_2^n - \{u\}$ has the homotopy type of $\dot{I}^n$, and hence is $(n-2)$-connected. Since $p \leq n - 1$, an application of Theorem 2.6.11 (with $X = T$, $Y = \dot{T}$, $n = p$, $W = \operatorname{Int} I_2^n - \{S_1\}$, $\phi = f^{-1} \circ \phi$) yields that $f^{-1} \circ \phi|\dot{T}$ has an extension $g:T \to \operatorname{Int}_2^n - \{S_1\}$. Define $h:T \times I \to \operatorname{Int} I_2^n$ by $h(s,t) = (1-t)f^{-1}(\phi(s)) + tg(s)$, whose image is in $\operatorname{Int} I_2^n$ because of the convexity of the latter; then h is a homotopy of $f^{-1} \circ \phi|T$ to g which keeps each point of $\dot{T}$ fixed. Now define $h':I^p \times I \to E^n \cup W$ by

$$h'(s,t) = \begin{cases} \phi(s) & s \in I^p - T \\ f(h(s,t)) & s \in T \end{cases}$$

Let us recall that $V \subset \operatorname{Int} E^n$. If $\phi^{-1}(V)$ met $\dot{I}^p$, then $\phi(\dot{I}^p) \cap \operatorname{Int} E^n \neq \phi$; so $X^{n-1} \cap \operatorname{Int} E^n \neq \phi$. Therefore $\phi^{-1}(V) \cap \dot{I}^p = \phi$. Therefore $T \cap \dot{I}^p = \phi$. Therefore $h'|\dot{I}^p \times I = \phi|\dot{I}^p$, and thus h' is a homotopy of ϕ relative to $\dot{I}^p$. Now clearly $h'(I^p,1) \subset X - \{x\}$. But by reasoning similar to that of 2.6.3, $E^n - \{x\}$ has $\dot{E}^n$ as a deformation retract, and therefore $h'|I^p \times \{1\}$ is homotopic relative to $\dot{I}^p$ to a map h^n such that $h^n(I^p) \subset X^{n-1}$. The proof is complete.

As a corollary we obtain the following theorem.

THEOREM 2.6.13. *If (X,Y) is a relative* CW *complex and X is connected, then (X^n,X^{n-1}) is $(n-1)$-connected for $n \geq 1$.*

PROOF. Let $\phi:(I^p,\dot{I}^p) \to (X^n,X^{n-1})$ be a map. Then $\phi(I^p)$ is compact, and therefore by Corollary 2.6.6 we may assume that (X,Y) is finite and prove our result by induction on the number k of n-cells of (X,Y). The case $k = 1$ is Lemma 2.6.12. Let us assume that the theorem is proved for $k = i$. Let the n-cells in question be $E_1^n, \cdots, E_{i+1}^n$, and set $W_0 = X^{n-1}$, $W_1 = X^{n-1} \cup E_1^n, \cdots, W_{i+1} = W_i \cup E_{i+1}^n$. Then by Lemma 2.6.12 with $X = W_k$, $Y = W_{k-1}$, $k = 1, \cdots, i+1$, we have

$$\begin{cases} \pi_p(W_1,W_0) = 0 \\ \pi_p(W_2,W_1) = 0 \\ \cdots\cdots\cdots\cdots\cdots \\ \pi_p(W_{i+1},W_i) = 0 \end{cases}$$

Now by the induction hypothesis, $\pi_p(W_i,X^{n-1}) = 0$. But the sequence

$$\pi_p(W_i,X^{n-1}) \to \pi_p(W_{i+1},X^{n-1}) \to \pi_p(W_{i+1},W_i)$$

is exact (Theorem 1.6.14), and the two end groups are zero. Hence the middle one is zero, completing the induction.

COROLLARY 2.6.14. *If* (X,Y) *is a relative* CW *complex and* X *is connected, then* $\rho\colon\pi_n^*(X^n,X^{n-1}) \approx H_n(X^n,X^{n-1})$.

COROLLARY 2.6.15. *If* (X,Y) *is a relative* CW *complex and* X *is connected, then* $\pi_p(X,X^n) = 0$ *for* $p \leq n$.

PROOF. We first show by induction on k, that $\pi_p(X^{n+k},X^n) = 0$. This is true for $k = 1$. Assume it for k. Then in the sequence

$$\pi_p(X^{n+k},X^n) \to \pi_p(X^{n+k+1},X^n) \to \pi_p(X^{n+k+1},X^{n+k})$$

the first and third groups are zero. Hence $\pi_p(X^{n+k+1},X^n) = 0$.

Now let $\phi\colon(I^p,\dot{I}^p) \to (X,X^n)$; then by compactness $\phi(I^p) \subset X^{n+k}$ for some k. Since $\pi_p(X^{n+k},X^n) = 0$, it follows that ϕ represents the zero element of $\pi_p(X,X^n)$.

COROLLARY 2.6.16. *If* $n > p$, *then* $\pi_p(X^{n+1},Y) \approx \pi_p(X,Y)$ *under the inclusion map.*

PROBLEM 10. If (X,Y) is a relative CW complex, then $(X \times 0) \cup (Y \times I)$ is a retract of $X \times I$, and hence the homotopy extension theorem holds with simplicial complexes replaced by relative CW complexes.

Let (X,Y) be a relative CW complex, X-connected. Let

$$s_0 = (0,\cdots,0) \in I^n$$

For each n-cell E_α^n of (X,Y) let f_α^n be a characteristic map, and let $x_\alpha = f_\alpha^n(s_0)$. Let γ_α be the element of $\pi_n(X^n,X^{n-1},x_\alpha)$ represented by $f_\alpha^n(I^n,\dot{I}^n,s_0) \to (X^n,X^{n-1},x_\alpha)$. Finally, let $x_0 \in X^{n-1}$.

THEOREM 2.6.17. $\pi_n(X^n,X^{n-1},x_0)$ *is generated by the elements* $\bar{\theta}_\xi(\gamma_\alpha)$, $(\alpha \in J_n,\ \xi \in \pi_1(X^{n-1},x_0,x_\alpha))$.

PROOF. Suppose first that: (1) (X,Y) *is a simplicial decomposition of* (I^n,ϕ). If $n > 2$, $\pi_1(X^{n-1}) \approx \pi_1(X) = 0$; by the Hurewicz theorem $\rho\colon\pi_n(X^n,X^{n-1},x_0) \approx H_n(X^n,X^{n-1})$. Since $\rho(\bar{\theta}_\xi(\gamma_\alpha)) = e_\alpha^n$ and $H_n(X^n,X^{n-1})$ is generated by the e_α^n, it follows that $\pi_n(X^n,X^{n-1},x_0)$ is generated by the elements $\bar{\theta}_\xi(\gamma_\alpha)$. If $n = 2$, it follows from Seifert-Threlfall [B.4, Chapter 7], that $\pi_1(X^1,x_0)$ is the free group generated by the elements $\theta_{\xi_\alpha}(\partial_*\gamma_\alpha)$ where, for each α, θ_{ξ_α} is a fixed element of $\pi_1(X^{n-1},x_0,x_\alpha)$. Since the homotopy groups of X^2 vanish, $\partial_*\colon\pi_2(X^2,X^1,x_0) \approx \pi_1(X^1,x_0)$; since ∂_* is an operator isomorphism, it follows that the elements $\bar{\theta}_{\xi_\alpha}(\gamma_\alpha)$ generate $\pi_2(X^2,X^1,x_0)$.

We now drop Assumption 1 and assume instead the hypotheses of Lemma 2.6.12. Then by reasoning which is almost word for word the same as that in the proof of Lemma 2.6.12, except that $p = n$, we obtain that $f^{-1} \circ \phi|\dot{T}$ has an extension $g: T^{n-1} \to \text{Int } I^n - \{u\}$. Another application of Lemma 2.6.11 yields the existence of an extension h of g with

$$h:(T,T^{n-1}) \to (\text{Int } I^n, \text{Int } I^n - \{u\})$$

as in 2.6.12 $f^{-1} \circ \phi$ and h are then homotopic relative to $\dot{T}$. Hence ϕ is homotopic, relative to $\overline{I^n - T}$, to the map ϕ_1 such that

$$\phi_1(t) = \begin{cases} \phi(t) & t \in \overline{I^n - T} \\ f(h(t)) & t \in T \end{cases}$$

Choose $\epsilon > 0$ so small that, for each of the finite number of simplexes σ of K, $h(\dot{\sigma}) \cap I^n_\epsilon = \phi$, where $I^n_\epsilon = \{s \in I^n | |s| \leq \epsilon\}$. Now $\dot{I}^n$ is a deformation retract of $I^n - I^n_\epsilon$; let $\Delta: I^n \times I \to I^n$ be a map such that

$$\begin{cases} \Delta(s,0) = s & \\ \Delta(s,u) = s & s \in \dot{I}^n \\ \Delta(s,1) \in \dot{I}^n \text{ and } \Delta(s,u) \notin I^n_\epsilon & s \notin I^n_\epsilon \end{cases}$$

Define $\psi: I^n \times I \to X^n$ by

$$\psi(t,u) = \begin{cases} f(\Delta(h(t),u)) & t \in T \\ f(\Delta(f^{-1}(\phi(t)),u)) & t \in \overline{I^n - T},\ \phi(t) \in f(I^n) \\ \phi(t) & \phi(t) \notin f(I^n) \end{cases}$$

Then ψ is continuous, and

$$\psi(t,u) \begin{cases} = \phi_1(t) & u = 0 \\ = \phi(t) & t \in \dot{I}^n \\ \in X^n - \{x\} & t \in \overline{I^n - T} \end{cases}$$

Let $\phi_2(t) = \psi(t,1)$. Thus

$$\begin{cases} \phi_2(t) = \phi(t) & t \in \dot{I}^n \\ \phi_2(t) \in X^n - \{x\} & t \in \overline{I^n - T} \\ \phi_2(t) = f(h_1(t)) & t \in T \end{cases}$$

where $h_1:(T,T^{n-1}) \to (I^n,\dot{I}^n)$. Finally, since X^{n-1} is a deformation retreat of $X^n - \{x\}$, ϕ_2 is homotopic, relative to $\dot{I}^n \cup T$, to a map ϕ_3 such that

$$\begin{cases} \phi_3(t) = \phi(t) & t \in \dot{I}^n \\ \phi_3(t) \in X^{n-1} & t \in \overline{I^n - T} \\ \phi_3(t) = f(h_1(t)) & t \in T \end{cases}$$

and therefore ϕ is homotopic, relative to $\dot{I}^n$, to ϕ_3. The map ϕ_3 has the following property: If σ is an n-simplex of K, then either $\phi_3(\sigma) \subset X^{n-1}$ or $\phi_3|\sigma = f \circ h_\sigma$, where $h_\sigma:(\sigma,\dot{\sigma}) \to (I^n,\dot{I}^n)$. In particular, $\phi_3:(K^n,K^{n-1},s_0) \to (X^n,X^{n-1},x_\alpha)$.

Let η be the element of $\pi_n(K^n,K^{n-1},s_0)$ represented by the identity map of $(I^n,\dot{I}^n,s_0)$ into (K^n,K^{n-1},s_0). For each n-simplex σ of K, let t_σ be a vertex of σ, and let $\eta_\sigma \in \pi_n(K^n,K^{n-1},t_\sigma)$ be the element represented by a characteristic map for σ. Let $\gamma \in \pi_n(X^n,X^{n-1},x_\alpha)$ be the element represented by ϕ (and therefore by ϕ_3). Then $\gamma = \phi_{3*}(\eta)$. Now η is a sum of terms of the form $\bar{\theta}_{\xi_\sigma}(\eta_\sigma)$ with $\xi_\sigma \in \pi_1(K^{n-1},s_0,t_\sigma)$, and therefore γ is a sum of terms of the form $\phi_{3*}(\bar{\theta}_{\xi_\sigma}(\eta_\sigma)) = \bar{\theta}_{\xi'_\sigma}(\phi_{3*}(\eta_\sigma))$, where $\xi'_\sigma = \phi_{3*}(\xi_\sigma)$ (Remark 1.7.21). If $\phi_3(\sigma) \subset X^{n-1}$, then $\phi_{3*}(\eta_\sigma) = 0$; otherwise $\phi_{3*}(\eta_\sigma) = f_*(h_{\sigma*}(\eta_\sigma))$. But $\pi_n(I^n,\dot{I}^n,h_\sigma(t_\sigma))$ is the infinite cyclic group generated by $\bar{\theta}_{\zeta_\sigma}(\iota)$ where ι generates $\pi_n(I^n,\dot{I}^n,s_0)$ and ζ_σ is a fixed element of $\pi_1(\dot{I}^n,h_\sigma(t_\sigma),s_0)$. Thus $\phi_{3*}(\eta_\sigma) = f_*(n_\sigma\bar{\theta}_{\zeta_\sigma}(\iota)) = n_\sigma\bar{\theta}_{\zeta'_\sigma}(f_*(\iota)) = n_\sigma\bar{\theta}_{\zeta'_\sigma}(\gamma_\alpha)$, where $\zeta'_\sigma = f_*(\zeta_\sigma)$ and $n_\sigma \in Z$. Hence we finally see that γ is a sum of terms of the form $n_\sigma\bar{\theta}_{\xi'_\sigma\zeta'_\sigma}(\gamma_\alpha)$. This proves the theorem under the hypotheses of Lemma 2.6.12.

Now we make a third assumption: (X,Y) has a finite number of n-cells $E_1^n,\cdots,E_r^n$ and none of higher degree. Our conclusion is proved by induction on r. We have shown above that it holds for $r = 1$. Assume it for $r - 1$. Let $W = X^{n-1} \cup E_2^n \cup \cdots \cup E_r^n$. Consider the sequence

$$\pi_n(W,X^{n-1}) \xrightarrow{i_*} \pi_n(X^n,X^{n-1}) \xrightarrow{j_*} \pi_n(X^n,W) \rightarrow \pi_{n-1}(W,X^{n-1}) = 0$$

By induction hypothesis, $\pi_n(W,X^{n-1})$ is generated by the elements $\bar{\theta}_\xi(\gamma_\alpha)(\alpha = 2,\cdots,r;\ \xi \in \pi_1(X^{n-1},x_0,x_\alpha))$. Hence Image i_* = Kernel j_* is generated by the elements $i_*\bar{\theta}_\xi(\gamma_\alpha) = \bar{\theta}_\xi(i_*\gamma_\alpha) = \bar{\theta}_\xi(\gamma_\alpha)$. Now if $\gamma \in \pi_n(X^n,X^{n-1})$, then $j_*\gamma \in \pi_n(X^n,W)$ and (X^n,W) has only one n-cell E_1^n, and therefore $j_*\gamma = m\bar{\theta}_\xi(\gamma_1)$ with $\xi \in \pi_1(W,x_0,x_1)$, $m \in Z$. Choose $\xi' \in \pi_1(X^{n-1},x_0,x_1)$ such that $k_{*\xi'} = \xi$, where $k:X^{n-1} \rightarrow W$ is the inclusion map. Then $j_*(\gamma - m\bar{\theta}_{\xi'}(\gamma_1)) = m\bar{\theta}_\xi(\gamma_1) - m\bar{\theta}_\xi(\gamma_1) = 0$. Hence $\gamma - m\bar{\theta}_{\xi'}(\gamma_1)$ is a sum of terms of the form $\bar{\theta}_\xi(\gamma_\alpha)$ with $\alpha > 1$, and our result follows for the case where (X,Y) has a finite number of n-cells.

The general case now follows from the usual compactness argument.

DEFINITION. *Let* (X,Y) *and* (X_1,Y_1) *be relative* CW *complexes.* A map $\phi:(X,Y) \rightarrow (X_1,Y_1)$ *is said to be* cellular *if and only if* $\phi(X^n) \subset X_1^n$ *for all* n.

THEOREM 2.6.18. *Let* (X,Y) *and* (X_1,Y_1) *be relative* CW *complexes and let* $\phi:(X,Y) \rightarrow (X_1,Y_1)$ *be a map. Then* ϕ *is homotopic, relative to* Y, *to a cellular map* θ.

PROOF. We define inductively a sequence $F_p:X^p \times I \rightarrow X_1$ of maps such that

$$\begin{cases} F_p(x,0) = \phi(x) & \\ F_p(x,t) = \phi(x) & (x \in Y) \\ F_p(x,t) = F_{p-1}(x,t) & (x \in X^{p-1}) \\ F_p(X^p \times 1) \subset X_1^p & \end{cases}$$

Define $F_{-1}(x,t) = \phi(x)$ for $x \in X^{-1} = Y$. Suppose that F_p has been constructed. Let E_α^{p+1} be a $(p+1)$ cell of (X,Y), and let $f_\alpha^{p+1}: I^{p+1} \to E_\alpha^{p+1}$ be a characteristic map. Define $\psi: I^{p+1} \times 0 \cup \dot{I}^{p+1} \times I \to X_1$ by

$$\begin{aligned} \psi(u,0) &= \phi(f_\alpha^{p+1}(u)) & u &\in I^{p+1} \\ \psi(u,t) &= F_p(f_\alpha^{p+1}(u),t) & u &\in \dot{I}^{p+1} \end{aligned}$$

Then

$$\psi(\dot{I}^{p+1} \times 1) = F_p(\dot{E}_\alpha^{p+1} \times \{1\}) \subset X_1^p \subset X_1^{p+1}$$

But $\pi_{p+1}(X_1, X_1^{p+1}) = 0$, and therefore ψ has an extension $\psi: I^{p+1} \times I \to X_1$ such that $\psi(I^{p+1} \times 1) \subset X_1^{p+1}$. Therefore we may define F_{p+1}^α on $E_\alpha^{p+1} \times I$ by $F_{p+1}^\alpha(x,t) = \psi((f_\alpha^{p+1})^{-1}(x),t)$. If $\alpha \neq \beta$, then $E_\alpha^{p+1} \cap E_\beta^{p+1} \subset X^p$, whence $F_{p+1}^\alpha | E_\alpha^{p+1} \cap E_\beta^{p+1} = F_{p+1}^\beta | E_\alpha^{p+1} \cap E_\beta^{p+1} = F_p | E_\alpha^{p+1} \cap E_\beta^{p+1}$. Hence we may define F_{p+1} by

$$\begin{cases} F_{p+1} | E_\alpha^{p+1} \times I = F_{p+1}^\alpha \\ F_{p+1} | X^p \times I = F_p \end{cases}$$

Finally we define $F: X \times I \to X_1$ by

$$F | X^p \times I = F_p$$

Then F is the desired homotopy.

Let (X,Y) and (X_1,Y_1) be relative CW complexes and let $\phi:(X,Y) \to (X_1,Y_1)$ be a cellular map. Then $\phi:(X^n,X^{n-1}) \to (X_1^n, X_1^{n-1})$ and therefore f induces maps

$$\phi_{n*}: C_n(X,Y) \to C_n(X_1,Y_1)$$

for each n, thereby defining $\phi_*: C(X,Y) \to C(X_1,Y_1)$.

THEOREM 2.6.19. *The map $\phi_*: C(X,Y) \to C(X_1,Y_1)$ is a chain mapping and therefore induces homomorphisms $\phi_*: H_n(C(X,Y)) \to H_n(C(X_1,Y_1))$. Furthermore the diagram*

$$\begin{array}{ccc} H_n(C(X,Y)) & \xrightarrow{\phi_*} & H_n(C(X_1,Y_1)) \\ \downarrow \theta & & \downarrow \theta \\ H_n(X,Y) & \xrightarrow{\phi_*} & H_n(X_1,Y_1) \end{array}$$

is commutative, where the θ's are the isomorphisms of Theorem 2.6.10.

PROOF. If D is the diagram of the proof of Theorem 2.6.10, then f defines a map of D into D_1 and the resulting three-dimensional diagram is commutative. The statements of the theorem follow from this fact.

2.7 Obstruction Theory [3, 28]

We shall be concerned here with the extension and classification problems for maps of a CW complex into a space. The main tool will be the notion of *obstruction*, introduced by Eilenberg [3].

Let (X, Y) be a relative CW complex, W a space, and $\phi: Y \to W$ a map. We shall study the possibility of extending ϕ over X by the *step-wise extension process*; i.e., supposing ϕ to have been extended over X^n, to attempt to extend it over X^{n+1}. The obstruction cocycle measures the extent to which this further extendibility is impossible.

Let then $\phi: X^n \to W$ be a map, $n \geq 1$. We assume for simplicity that W is n-simple. Then if E_α^{n+1} is an $(n+1)$-cell of (X, Y) with characteristic map f_α^{n+1}, the map $\phi \circ f_\alpha^{n+1} | \dot{I}^{n+1}$, with the orientation $\partial_* \omega_{n+1}$, represents a unique element $c_\phi^{n+1}(e_\alpha^{n+1})$ of $\pi_n^*(W) \approx \pi_n(W)$. The function c_ϕ^{n+1} thus defined is a cochain of $C(X, Y)$ with coefficients in $\pi_n(W)$; it is called the *obstruction* to the extension of ϕ over X^{n+1}.

Before deriving properties of c_ϕ^{n+1}, we give an alternative description which will be useful later. Let $\hat{W}$ be the cone over W; then all the homotopy groups of $\hat{W}$ vanish, and it follows from Theorem 2.6.11 that ϕ has an extension $\hat{\phi}: (X, X^n) \to (\hat{W}, W)$. Now $\partial_*: \pi_{q+1}(\hat{W}, W) \approx \pi_q(W)$ for all q, and the n-simplicity of W implies the $(n+1)$-simplicity of $(\hat{W}, W)$.

Now consider the diagram

$$\begin{array}{ccc}
\pi_{n+1}^*(X^{n+1}, X^n) & \xrightarrow{\hat{\phi}_*} & \pi_{n+1}(\hat{W}, W) \\
\downarrow \rho & & \downarrow \partial_* \\
H_{n+1}(X^{n+1}, X^n) & & \pi_n(W)
\end{array}$$

Then the homomorphisms ρ and ∂_* are isomorphisms onto, and $C_\phi^{n+1} = \partial_* \circ \hat{\phi}_* \circ \rho^{-1}: C_{n+1}(X, Y) \to \pi_n(W)$.

THEOREM 2.7.1. *The cochain c_ϕ^{n+1} is a cocycle.*

PROOF. Consider the diagram

$$\begin{array}{ccccccc}
H_{n+2}(X^{n+2}, X^{n+1}) & \xleftarrow{\rho} & \pi_{n+2}^*(X^{n+2}, X^{n+1}) & & & & \\
\downarrow \partial_* & & \downarrow \partial_* & & & & \\
H_{n+1}(X^{n+1}) & \xleftarrow{\rho} & \pi_{n+1}^*(X^{n+1}) & \xrightarrow{\hat{\phi}_*} & \pi_{n+1}(\hat{W}) & & \\
\downarrow j_* & & \downarrow j_* & & \downarrow j_* & & \\
H_{n+1}(X^{n+1}, X^n) & \xleftarrow{\rho} & \pi_{n+1}^*(X^{n+1}, X^n) & \xrightarrow{\hat{\phi}_*} & \pi_{n+1}(\hat{W}, W) & \xrightarrow{\partial_*} & \pi_n(W)
\end{array}$$

Now

$$\begin{aligned}
\delta c_\phi^{n+1} &= c_\phi^{n+1} \circ \partial = c_\phi^{n+1} \circ j_* \circ \partial_* = \partial_* \circ \hat{\phi}_* \circ \rho^{-1} \circ j_* \circ \partial_* \\
&= \partial_* \circ \hat{\phi}_* \circ j_* \circ \partial_* \circ \rho^{-1} = \partial_* \circ j_* \circ \hat{\phi}_* \circ \partial_* \circ \rho^{-1} = 0
\end{aligned}$$

since $\pi_{n+1}(\hat{W}) = 0$.

REMARK. *In the proof we make use of the fact that* $j_*:\pi_{n+1}(X^{n+1}) \to \pi_{n+1}(X^{n+1},X^n)$ *maps* $\Omega_{n+1}(X^{n+1})$ *into* $\bar{\Omega}_{n+1}(X^{n+1},X^n)$. *This follows from the fact that the homomorphism* $\pi_1(X^n) \to \pi_1(X^{n+1})$ *induced by the inclusion map is onto, since* $\pi_1(X^{n+1},X^n) = 0$. *Hence* $\Omega_{n+1}(X^{n+1})$ *is the subgroup generated by the elements* $\alpha - \theta_\xi(\alpha)$, $\xi \in \pi_1(X^{n+1})$, $\alpha \in \pi_{n+1}(X^{n+1})$, *and this is the subgroup generated by the elements* $\alpha - \theta_{i_*(\xi)}(\alpha)$ *with* $\xi \in \pi_1(X^n)$, $\alpha \in \pi_{n+1}(X^{n+1})$. *The latter subgroup is mapped into* $\bar{\Omega}_{n+1}(X^{n+1},X^n)$ *by* j_* *since* j_* *is an operator homomorphism with respect to* $\pi_1(X^n)$.

THEOREM 2.7.2. *The cocycle* c_ϕ^{n+1} *has the following additional properties:*

1. $c_\phi^{n+1}(e_\alpha^{n+1}) = 0$ *if and only if* ϕ *can be extended over* $E_\alpha^{n+1} \cup X^n$.
2. $c_\phi^{n+1} = 0$ *if and only if* ϕ *can be extended over* X^{n+1}.
3. *If* $\phi,\theta: X^n \to W$ *are homotopic maps, then* $c_\phi^{n+1} = c_\theta^{n+1}$.
4. *Let* W' *be n-simple,* $h: W \to W'$ *a map. Then*
$$c_{h*\phi}^{n+1} = h \underset{*}{\circ} c_\phi^{n+1}$$
5. *Let* (X_1, Y_1) *be another* CW *complex,* $g:(X_1,Y_1) \to (X,Y)$ *a cellular map. Then*
$$c_{\phi\circ g|X_1^n}^{n+1} = c_\phi^{n+1} \circ g_*$$
where $g_*: C_{n+1}(X_1,Y_1) \to C_{n+1}(X,Y)$ *is the chain map defined by* g.

PROOF. Parts 1, 2, and 3 are trivial. To prove Part 4 let $\hat{h}: \hat{W} \to \hat{W}'$ be an extension of h. Then $\hat{h} \circ \hat{\phi}:(X,X^n) \to (\hat{W}',W')$ is an extension of $h \circ \phi$ and therefore

$$\begin{array}{ccccc}
\pi_{n+1}^*(X^{n+1},X^n) & \xrightarrow{\hat{\phi}_*} & \pi_{n+1}(\hat{W},W) & \xrightarrow{\hat{h}_*} & \pi_{n+1}(\hat{W}',W') \\
\downarrow \rho & & \downarrow \partial_* & & \downarrow \partial_* \\
C_{n+1}(X,Y) & & \pi_n(W) & \xrightarrow{h_*} & \pi_n(W')
\end{array}$$

it follows from the commutativity of the foregoing diagram that

$$\begin{aligned} c_{h\circ\phi}^{n+1} &= \partial_* \circ (\hat{h} \circ \hat{f})_* \circ \rho^{-1} = \partial_* \circ \hat{h}_* \circ \hat{\phi}_* \circ \rho^{-1} = h_* \circ \partial_* \circ \hat{\phi}_* \circ \rho^{-1} \\ &= h_* \circ c_\phi^{n+1} \end{aligned}$$

To prove Part 5, note that $\hat{\phi} \circ g:(X_1,X_1^n) \to (\hat{W},W)$ is an extension of $\phi \circ g|X_1^n$, and our result follows from the commutativity of the diagram

$$\begin{array}{ccccc}
\pi_*^{n+1}(X_1^{n+1},X_1^n) & \xrightarrow{g_*} & \pi_{n+1}^*(X^{n+1},X^n) & \xrightarrow{\hat{\phi}_*} & \pi_{n+1}(\hat{W},W) \\
\downarrow \rho & & \downarrow \rho & & \downarrow \partial_* \\
C_{n+1}(X_1,Y_1) & \xrightarrow{g_*} & C_{n+1}(X,Y) & & \pi_n(W)
\end{array}$$

by a similar argument. Q.E.D.

In order to study the analogous situation for the classification problem, we need some information about the relationship between the CW structure of (X,Y) and that of $(I \times X, I \times Y)$.

Let E^n_α be an n-cell of X with characteristic map f^n_α. We define characteristic maps ${}^0f^n_\alpha$, ${}^1f^n_\alpha$, ${}^If^n_\alpha$ for the cells $\{0\} \times E^n_\alpha$, $\{1\} \times E^n_\alpha$, $I \times E^n_\alpha$ by

$$\begin{cases} {}^0f^n_\alpha(u) = (0, f^n_\alpha(u)) \\ {}^1f^n_\alpha(u) = (1, f^n_\alpha(u)) \end{cases} \quad (u \in I^n)$$
$${}^If^n_\alpha(t,u) = (t, f^n_\alpha(u)) \qquad (t \in I,\ u \in I^n)$$

We denote by $0 \times e^n_\alpha$, $1 \times e^n_\alpha$, $I \times e^n_\alpha$ the chains of $(I \times X, I \times Y)$ defined by these characteristic maps. If $c \in C_n(X,Y)$, we define $0 \times c$, $1 \times c$, $I \times c$ by linearity.

Lemma 2.7.3. *The following relations hold in* $C(I \times X, I \times Y)$:

$$\begin{cases} \partial(0 \times e^n_\alpha) = 0 \times \partial e^n_\alpha \\ \partial(1 \times e^n_\alpha) = 1 \times \partial e^n_\alpha \\ \partial(I \times e^n_\alpha) = 1 \times e^n_\alpha - 0 \times e^n_\alpha - I \times \partial e^n_\alpha \end{cases}$$

PROOF. The first two follow from the fact that the map $x \to (i,x)$ $(i = 0,1)$ is a homeomorphism of X onto $\{i\} \times X$ which is an isomorphism of the CW complex (X,Y) onto the subcomplex

$$(\{i\} \times X, \{i\} \times Y)$$

of $(I \times X, I \times Y)$.

We first prove the third statement in a special case. Let K^n be the usual CW decomposition of I^n; then $K^{n+1} = I \times K^n$. On the other hand, it is clear that

$$\begin{cases} e^n_{1,0} = 0 \times e^n \\ e^n_{1,1} = 1 \times e^n \\ e^n_{i,\epsilon} = I \times e^{n-1}_{i-1,\epsilon}, \qquad i = 2,\cdots,n+1 \end{cases}$$

Hence

$$\begin{aligned} \partial e^{n+1} &= \sum_{i=1}^{n+1} \sum_{\epsilon=0}^{1} (-1)^{i+\epsilon} e^n_{i,\epsilon} \\ &= e^n_{1,1} - e^n_{1,0} + \sum_{\substack{i>1 \\ \epsilon}} (-1)^{i+\epsilon} e^n_{i,\epsilon} \\ &= 1 \times e^n - 0 \times e^n - \sum_{i>1} (-1)^{i+\epsilon}\, I \times e^{n-1}_{i-1,\epsilon} \\ &= 1 \times e^n - 0 \times e^n - I \times \partial e^n \end{aligned}$$

In the general case, we first note that $f^n_\alpha:(I^n,\dot{I}^n) \to (X^n,X^{n-1})$ is homotopic to a cellular map $f:(I^n,\dot{I}^n) \to (X^n,X^{n-1})$. Then ${}^If_*(e^{n+1}) = I \times e^n_\alpha$, and therefore

$$\begin{aligned}\partial(I \times e^n_\alpha) &= \partial^I f_*(e^{n+1}) = {}^I f_* \partial(e^{n+1}) \\ &= {}^I f_*(1 \times e^n - 0 \times e^n - I \times \partial e^n) \\ &= 1 \times f_* e^n - 0 \times f_* e^n - I \times f_* \partial e^n \\ &= 1 \times e^n_\alpha - 0 \times e^n_\alpha - I \times \partial e^n_\alpha \end{aligned}$$

Q.E.D.

Now let $\phi,\theta: X^n \to W$ be maps, and let $F: I \times X^{n-1} \to W$ be a homotopy of $\phi|X^{n-1}$ to $\theta|X^{n-1}$. Let $X_* = I \times X$, $Y_* = \dot{I} \times X \cup I \times Y$. Define $F_1: X^n_* \to W$ by

$$\begin{cases} F_1(0,x) = \phi(x) \\ F_1(1,x) = \theta(x) \end{cases} \quad (x \in X^n) \qquad F_1(t,x) = F(t,x) \quad x \in X^{n-1}$$

We now define a cochain $d^n_{\phi,F,\theta} \in C^n(X,Y;\pi_n(W))$ by

$$d^n_{\phi,F,\theta}(e^n_\alpha) = c^{n+1}_{F_1}(I \times e^n_\alpha)$$

If $\phi|X^{n-1} = \theta|X^{n-1}$ and $F(t,x) = \phi(x) = \theta(x)$ for $x \in X^{n-1}$, we denote $d^n_{\phi,F,\theta}$ simply by $d^n_{\phi,\theta}$. In any case,

$$\begin{aligned} c^{n+1}_{F_1}(0 \times e^n_\alpha) &= c^{n+1}_\phi(e^n_\alpha) \\ c^{n+1}_{F_1}(1 \times e^n_\alpha) &= c^{n+1}_\theta(e^n_\alpha) \end{aligned}$$

THEOREM 2.7.4. $\delta d^n_{\phi,F,\theta} = c^{n+1}_\theta - c^{n+1}_\phi$.

PROOF. We have

$$\begin{aligned} \delta d^n_{\phi,F,\theta}(e^{n+1}_\alpha) &= d^n_{\phi,F,\theta}(\partial e^{n+1}_\alpha) = c^{n+1}_{F_1}(I \times \partial e^{n+1}_\alpha) \\ &= c^{n+1}_{F_1}(1 \times e^{n+1}_\alpha - 0 \times e^{n+1}_\alpha - \partial(I \times e^{n+1}_\alpha)) \\ &= c^{n+1}_\theta(e^{n+1}_\alpha) - c^{n+1}_\phi(e^{n+1}_\alpha) - \delta c^{n+1}_{F_1}(I \times e^{n+1}_\alpha) \\ &= c^{n+1}_\theta(e^{n+1}_\alpha) - c^{n+1}_\phi(e^{n+1}_\alpha) \end{aligned}$$

since $c^{n+1}_{F_1}$ is a cocycle. Q.E.D.

LEMMA 2.7.5. *Let $\phi_0,\phi_1,\phi_2: X^n \to W$ be maps, and let*

$$F_{i,i+1}: I \times X^{n-1} \to W$$

be a homotopy of $\phi_i|X^{n-1}$ to $\phi_{i+1}|X^{n-1}$ $(i = 0,1)$. Define $F_{02}: I \times X^{n-1} \to W$ by

$$(*) \qquad F_{02}(t,x) = \begin{cases} F_{01}(2t,x) & 0 \le t \le \frac{1}{2} \\ F_{12}(2t-1,x) & \frac{1}{2} \le t \le 1 \end{cases}$$

Then

$$d^n_{\phi_0,F_{01},\phi_1} + d^n_{\phi_1,F_{12},\phi_2} = d^n_{\phi_0,F_{02},f_2}$$

PROOF. Let $\hat{F}_{i,i+1}: I \times X^n \to \hat{W}$ be a map such that

$$\begin{cases} \hat{F}_{i,i+1}(0,x) = \phi_i(x) \\ \hat{F}_{i,i+1}(1,x) = \phi_{i+1}(x) \end{cases} \quad (x \in X^n) \qquad \hat{F}_{i,i+1}(t,x) = F_{i,i+1}(t,x) \quad (x \in X^{n-1})$$

Define $\hat{F}_{02}: I \times X^n \to \hat{W}$ by (*) with $\hat{F}_{ij}$ in place of F_{ij}. Let e^n_α be an n-cell of (X, Y) with characteristic map f, and let ${}^I f$ be the corresponding characteristic map for $I \times e^n_\alpha$. Let γ_{ij} be the element of $\pi_{n+1}(\hat{W}, W)$ represented by $G_{ij} = \hat{F}_{ij} \circ {}^I f: (I^{n+1}, \dot{I}^{n+1}) \to (\hat{W}, W)$. Since ${}^I f(t,u) = (t, f(u))$, it follows that $G_{02} = G_{01} + G_{12}$ and therefore $\gamma_{02} = \gamma_{01} + \gamma_{12}$. But it is easily verified that

$$d^n_{\phi_i, F_{ij}, \phi_j}(e^n_\alpha) = \partial_* \gamma_{ij}$$

and our result follows.

LEMMA 2.7.6. *Let $\psi: J^n \to W$ be a map and let $\gamma \in \pi_n(W)$. Then there is an extension $\psi_1: \dot{I}^{n+1} \to W$ such that ψ_1 represents γ.*

PROOF. Since J^n is contractible, there is a representative $\phi: \dot{I}^{n+1} \to W$ such that $\phi(J^n)$ is a single point $w_0 \in W$, and there is a map $\psi: I \times J^n \to W$ such that

$$\begin{cases} \psi(1,u) = \psi(u) \\ \psi(0,u) = w_0 \end{cases}$$

By the homotopy extension theorem, there is a map $\Phi: I \times \dot{I}^{n+1} \to W$ such that

$$\begin{aligned} \Phi(0,u) &= \phi(u) \\ \Phi(t,u) &= \psi(t,u) \qquad u \in J^n \end{aligned}$$

Define $\psi_1(u) = \Phi(1,u)$. Then ϕ is homotopic to ψ_1, whence ψ_1 is a representative of γ.

THEOREM 2.7.7. *Let $\phi: X^n \to W$ be a map and let $d \in C^n(X, Y; \pi_n(W))$. Then there is a map $\theta: X^n \to W$ such that*

1. $\phi | X^{n-1} = \theta | X^{n-1}$.
2. $d^n_{\phi,\theta} = d$.

PROOF. Define $\phi | X^{n-1}$ by Part 1. Let E^n_α be an n-cell of (X, Y) and f^n_α a characteristic map for E^n_α. Define $\psi: J^n \to W$ by

$$\psi(t,u) = \phi(f^n_\alpha(u)) \qquad (t,u) \in J^n$$

Let $\psi_1: \dot{I}^{n+1} \to W$ be an extension of ψ which represents the element $d(e^n_\alpha)$. Define $\theta_\alpha: E^n_\alpha \to W$ by

$$\theta_\alpha(x) = \psi_1(1, (f^n_\alpha)^{-1}(x))$$

and define $\theta: X^n \to W$ by

$$\theta | E^n_\alpha = \theta_\alpha$$

Then clearly $d^n_{\phi,\theta}(e^n_\alpha) = d(e^n_\alpha)$ for all α, whence $d^n_{\phi,\theta} = d$.

THEOREM 2.7.8. *Let $\phi: X^n \to W$ be a map. Then $\phi|X^{n-1}$ can be extended to a map of X^{n+1} into W if and only if $c_\phi^{n+1} \in B^{n+1}(X, Y; \pi_n(W))$.*

PROOF. Let $\theta_1: X^{n+1} \to W$ be an extension of $\phi|X^{n-1}$, and let $\theta = \theta_1|X^n$. Then

$$\delta d_{\phi,\theta}^n = c_\theta^{n+1} - c_\phi^{n+1}$$

But $c_\theta^{n+1} = 0$, since θ has the extension θ_1, and therefore $c_\phi^{n+1} = \delta(-d_{\phi,\theta}^n)$.

Conversely, let $c_\phi^{n+1} = \delta d$ with $d \in C^n(X, Y; \pi_n(W))$. By Theorem 2.7.7, there is a map $\theta: X^n \to W$ with $d_{\phi,\theta}^n = -d$. Then

$$c_\theta^{n+1} = c_\phi^{n+1} + \delta d_{\phi,\theta}^n = c_\phi^{n+1} - \delta d = 0$$

and therefore θ has an extension $\theta_1: X^{n+1} \to W$.

LEMMA 2.7.9. *Let (X, Y) be a relative* CW *complex. Let $X^* = I \times X$, $Y^* = I \times Y \cup \dot{I} \times X$. Then the map $\sigma_p: C_p(X, Y) \to C_{p+1}(X^*, Y^*)$ given by*

$$\sigma_p(e_\alpha^p) = I \times e_\alpha^p$$

is an isomorphism onto and $\partial \circ \sigma_p = -\sigma_{p-1} \circ \partial$. Hence $H_p(X, Y) \approx H_{p+1}(X^*, Y^*)$.

PROOF. The cells $0 \times E_\beta^{p+1}$ and $1 \times E^{p+1}$ belonging to Y^*, the map $E_\alpha^p \to I \times E_\alpha^p$ is a 1:1 correspondence between the p-cells of (X, Y) and the $(p+1)$-cells of (X^*, Y^*). Hence σ_p is an isomorphism onto. Now

$$\begin{aligned}\partial\sigma_p(e_\alpha^p) &= \partial(I \times e_\alpha^p) = 1 \times e_\alpha^p - 0 \times e_\alpha^p - I \times \partial e_\alpha^p \\ &= -I \times \partial e_\alpha^p = -\sigma_{p-1}(\partial e_\alpha^p)\end{aligned}$$

The last statement follows immediately.

THEOREM 2.7.10. *Let $\phi, \theta: X \to W$ be maps such that $\phi|X^{n-1} = \theta|X^{n-1}$. Then*

1. *$d_{\phi,\theta}^n \in Z^n(X, Y; \pi_n(W))$.*
2. *$d_{\phi,\theta}^n = 0$ if and only if $\phi|X^n$ is homotopic to $\theta|X^n$, relative to X^{n-1}.*
3. *$d_{\phi,\theta}^n \in B^n(X, Y; \pi_n(W))$ if and only if $\phi|X^n$ is homotopic to $\theta|X^n$* rel X^{n-2}.

PROOF. Define $F: X^{*n} \to W$ by

$$\begin{aligned}F(0,x) &= \phi(x),\ F(1,x) = \theta(x) \qquad (x \in X)\\ F(t,x) &= \phi(x) = \theta(x) \qquad (x \in X^{n-1})\end{aligned}$$

From the definition of $d_{\phi,\theta}$ it follows that

$$\sigma_{n+1}^* c_F = d_{\phi,\theta}$$

where σ_{n+1}^* is the cochain map defined by σ. Our result now follows from Theorem 2.7.8 and Lemma 2.7.9.

2.8 Extension and Classification Theorems [3, 10, 22, 30]

Let (X, Y) be a relative CW complex, W an $(n - 1)$ connected space, and $f: Y \to W$ a map. Suppose that W is n-simple. (If $n > 1$, this hypothesis follows from $(n - 1)$-connectedness.)

LEMMA 2.8.1. *Let $f', f'': X^n \to W$ be two extensions of f. Then $f'|x^{n-1}$ and $f''|X^{n-1}$ are homotopic* rel Y.

PROOF. Suppose that f' and f'' coincide on X^p and $p < n - 1$. Then $d_{f',f''} = d^{p+1}_{f',f''}$ is defined and belongs to $Z^{p+1}(X, Y; \pi_{p+1}(W))$. Since $\pi_{p+1}(W) = 0$, $d_{f',f''} = 0$ and $\therefore$ $f'|X^{p+1}$ and $f''|X^{p+1}$ are homotopic rel X^p. By the homotopy extension theorem (Theorem 1.0.1 and Problem 8), f' is homotopic rel X^p to a map f'_1 such that $f'_1|X^{p+1} = f''|X^{p+1}$. The proof now proceeds by induction.

LEMMA 2.8.2. *Let $f', f'': X^n \to W$ be extensions of f. Then $c_{f'} - c_{f''}$ $(= c^{n+1}_{f'} - c^{n+1}_{f''}) \in B^{n+1}(X, Y; \pi_n(W))$.*

PROOF. By Lemma 2.8.1, f'' is homotopic rel Y to a map f''_1 such that $f'|X^{n-1} = f''_1|X^{n-1}$. Then $c_{f''_1} = c_{f''}$, by Theorem 2.7.2. But by Theorem 2.7.4, we have

$$\delta d^n_{f',f''_1} = c_{f'} - c_{f''_1} = c_{f'} - c_{f''} \qquad \text{Q.E.D.}$$

It follows from Lemma 2.8.2 that we can define a cohomology class $\gamma^{n+1}(f) \in H^{n+1}(X, Y; \pi_n(W))$ by the following:

$\gamma^{n+1}(f)$ *is the cohomology class of $c_{f'}$ for any extension $f': X^n \to W$ of f.* $\gamma^{n+1}(f)$ is called the *primary obstruction* to the extension of f. Clearly $\gamma^{n+1}(f)$ is a homotopy invariant of f.

Define dim (X, Y) to be the least upper bound of the dimensionalities of the cells of (X, Y). Then we have the following Theorem.

THEOREM 2.8.3. (Extension Theorem.) *Suppose that W is q-simple and that $H^{q+1}(X, Y; \pi_q(W)) = 0$ for $n + 1 \leq q <$ dim (X, Y). Then f has an extension $\bar{f}: X \to W$ if and only if $\gamma^{n+1}(f) = 0$.*

PROOF. If f is extendible, then $\gamma^{n+1}(f) = 0$. Suppose that $\gamma^{n+1}(f) = 0$. Let $f_n: X^n \to W$ be an extension of f. Then c_{f_n} is a coboundary. Hence $f_n|X^{n-1}$ has an extension $f_{n+1}: X^{n+1} \to W$.

Suppose that $n + 1 \leq q <$ dim (X, Y) and that $f_q: X^q \to W$ is an extension of f. Then $c_f \in Z^{q+1}(X, Y; \pi_q(W)) = B^{q+1}(X, Y, \pi_q(W))$, so that c_{f_q} is a coboundary. Hence $f_q|X^{q-1}$ has an extension $f_{q+1}: X^{q+1} \to W$.

If dim (X,Y) is finite, we are through, for we may take $\bar{f} = f_{\dim(X,Y)}$. If dim (X,Y) is infinite, we have constructed a sequence $\{f_q : X^q \to Y\}$ of mappings such that

$$f_{q+1}|X^{q-1} = f_q|X^{q-1}$$

It follows that, for any $q, f_r|X^q = f_{q+1}|X^q$ for all $r \geq q+1$. Accordingly we may define

$$\bar{f}: X \to W$$

by

$$\bar{f}|X^q = f_{q+1}|X^q$$

Suppose now that $f,g: X \to W$ are maps such that $f|Y = g|Y$. Define $F: Y^* \to W$ by

$$\begin{cases} F(t,x) = f(x) = g(x) & x \in Y \\ \left.\begin{aligned} F(0,x) &= f(x) \\ F(1,x) &= g(x) \end{aligned}\right\} & x \in X \end{cases}$$

Then we can apply the preceding extension theory to the map F. We define $\delta^n(f,g) = \sigma^*\gamma^{n+1}(F) \in H^n(X,Y;\pi_n(W))$. To compute $\delta^n(f,g)$, note that F has an extension $F_1: X^{*n} \to W$, which is a homotopy of $f|X^{n-1}$ to $g|X^{n-1}$, and that $c_{F_1}^{n+1} = d_{f,F_1,g}^n$.

THEOREM 2.8.4. (Homotopy Theorem.) *Suppose that W is q-simple, and that $H^q(X,Y;\pi_q(W)) = 0$ for $n+1 \leq q < 1 + \dim(X,Y)$. Then f and g are homotopic* rel Y *if and only if $\delta^n(f,g) = 0$.*

PROOF. Follows from Theorem 2.8.3 and the foregoing remarks.

THEOREM 2.8.5. (Classification Theorem.) *Let (X,Y) be a relative* CW *complex and W an $(n-1)$-connected space. Suppose that*

$$\begin{cases} W \text{ is } q\text{-simple for } n+1 \leq q < 1 + \dim(X,Y) \\ H^q(X,Y;\pi_q(W)) = 0 \text{ for } n+1 \leq q < 1 + \dim(X,Y) \\ H^{q+1}(X,Y;\pi_q(W)) = 0 \text{ for } n+1 \leq q < \dim(X,Y) \end{cases}$$

Let $f_0: Y \to W$ be a map; $\gamma^{n+1}(f_0) = 0$. Then the homotopy classes rel Y *of the maps of X into W which extend f_0 are in* 1:1 *correspondence with the elements of $H^n(X,Y;\pi_n(W))$.*

PROOF. Let $f: X \to W$ be an extension of f_0; such an f exists by the extension theorem. If g is an extension of f_0, let $\phi(g) = \delta^n(g,f)$. By the homotopy theorem, if g_1,g_2 are extensions of f_0, then $g_1 \simeq g_2$ rel Y if and only if $0 = \delta^n(g_2,g_1) = \delta^n(g_2,f) - \delta^n(g_1,f)$. Hence the correspondence induced by ϕ is 1:1 into.

Let $d \in Z^n(X,Y;\pi_n(W))$. By Theorem 2.7.7 there is a map $g_1:X^n \to W$ such that $g_1|X^{n-1} = f|X^{n-1}$ and $d^n_{g_1,f} = d$. Then $c^{n+1}_{g_1} = c^{n+1}_f + \delta d^n_{g_1,f} = 0$. Now if $q \geq n+1$, $H^{q+1}(X,X^n;\pi_q(W)) = H^{q+1}(X,Y;\pi_q(W)) = 0$; by the extension theorem, g_1 has an extension $g:X \to W$. Clearly $\delta^n(g,f) =$ the cohomology class of d. Hence ϕ is onto.

COROLLARY 2.8.6. *The foregoing conclusion holds if either*

1. $\pi_q(W) = 0$ *for* $n + 1 \leq q < 1 + \dim(X,Y)$

or

2. $\dim(X,Y) \leq n$.

The classification and extension theorems were first proved by Hopf [10, p. 39], in 1933. Hopf stated the theorems for the absolute case, took X to be a simplicial polyhedron of maximum degree n and $W = S^n$. His version was stated in terms of homology, using the "degree" of the mappings f and g; Hurewicz [14 (1936, p. 117)] extended the results so that W could be any ANR; and Whitney [29, p. 51], was the first to state them in their present cohomological form, although he still retained Assumption 2 of Corollary 2.8.6 and stated the results in absolute form. The absolute case in its present form, with X simplicial, was first proved by Eilenberg [3, p. 231] who also introduced the notion of obstruction in the same paper.

We now associate with the $(n-1)$-connected, n-simple space W a cohomology class $\delta^n(W)$, which plays an important role in what follows.

LEMMA 2.8.7. *Let C be a free chain complex such that* $H_{n-1}(C)$ *is a free abelian group. Then*

$$H^n(C;G) \approx \text{Hom}\,\{H_n(C),G\}$$

PROOF. Let $f \in Z^n(C;G)$, so that $f:C_n \to G$ is a homomorphism and $f \circ \partial: C_{n+1} \to G$ is trivial. Then $f:(Z_n(C),B_n(C)) \to (G,0)$, and therefore f induces a homomorphism $\bar{f}:H_n(C) \to G$:

$$\bar{f}(z + B_n(C)) = f(z)$$

Clearly $\overline{f+g} = \bar{f} + \bar{g}$, and therefore the correspondence $f \to \bar{f}$ is a homomorphism $\phi:Z^n(C;G) \to \text{Hom}\,\{H_n(C),G\}$.

Let $h \in \text{Hom}\,\{H_n(C);G\}$. Then h defines a homomorphism $h_1:Z_n(C) \to G$;

$$h_1(z) = h(z + B_n(C))$$

Now $\partial: C_n \to C_{n-1}$ is a homomorphism with kernel $Z_n(C)$. Since C_{n-1} is free, we have $C_n = Z_n(C) \oplus P_n$, where $\partial: P_n \approx B_{n-1}(C) \subset C_{n-1}$. Therefore we may extend h_1 to a homomorphism $f: C_n \to G$ by

$$\begin{cases} f|Z_n(C) = h_1 \\ f(P_n) \quad = 0 \end{cases}$$

Then $f \in C^n(C;G)$ and $f(B_n(C)) = h(B_n(C)) = 0$, so that $\delta f = 0$, and $\bar{f} = h$. Hence ϕ is onto.

Let $f \in Z^n(C;G)$ and suppose that $\bar{f} = 0$; i.e., $f(Z_n(C)) = 0$. Thus $f:(C_n, Z_n(C)) \to (G,0)$, and therefore there is a homomorphism

$$h: B_{n-1}(C) \to G$$

such that $h \circ \partial = f$. Since $H_{n-1}(C)$ is free, $B_{n-1}(C)$ is a direct factor of $Z_{n-1}(C)$, and since $B_{n-2}(C)$ is free, $Z_{n-1}(C)$ is a direct factor of C_{n-1}. Hence $B_{n-1}(C)$ is a direct factor of C_{n-1}, and therefore h can be extended to a homomorphism $g: C_{n-1} \to G$. Then $g \in C^{n-1}(C;G)$ and $\delta g = f$. Hence ϕ is an isomorphism into. Q.E.D.

If W is an $(n-1)$-connected n-simple space, then $\rho: \pi_n(W) \approx H_n(W)$ and therefore $\rho^{-1}: H_n(W) \to \pi_n(W)$ is a homomorphism. Since $H_{n-1}(W) = 0$ if $n > 1$ and $H_{n-1}(W) = Z$ if $n = 1$, there is a unique $\delta^n(W) \in H^n(W;\pi_n(W))$ which induces the homomorphism ρ^{-1}.

We give another description of $\delta^n(W)$. Since W is $(n-1)$-connected, the total cubical complex $C(W)$ is chain-equivalent to its subcomplex $C^{n-1}(W,w_0)$. If $f:(I^n,\dot{I}^n) \to (W,w_0)$ is a cube in $Q^{n-1}(W,w_0)$, we assign to f the element $d^n(f) \in \pi_n(W,w_0)$ represented by f. Then $d^n \in Z^n(C^{n-1}(W,w_0); \pi_n(W))$ and it is clear from the proof of the Hurewicz theorem that the cohomology class of $H^n(W;\pi_n(W))$ which corresponds to $d^n(f)$ is $\delta^n(W)$.

If W is the space of a simplicial complex K, then $\delta^n(W)$ is finitely computable. For let $C_n(K) = Z_n(K) \oplus P$, where P is a subgroup such that $\partial: P \approx B_{n-1}(K)$. Such a decomposition can be found, for example, by the usual reduction of the incidence matrices to normal form. Define $d^n: C_n(K) \to \pi_n(W)$ by

$$d^n(P) = 0$$
$$d^n|Z_n(K) = \rho^{-1} \circ \pi$$

where $\pi: Z_n(K) \to H_n(K)$ is the natural homomorphism. It is then clear that the homomorphism of $H_n(K)$ into $\pi_n(W)$ induced by d^n is ρ^{-1}. Hence $\delta^n(W)$ is the cohomology class of d^n.

THEOREM 2.8.8. *Let (X, Y) be a relative* CW *complex, $f: Y \to W$ a map. Suppose that W is $(n-1)$-connected and n-simple. Then*

$$\gamma^{n+1}(f) = \delta^* f^* \delta^n(W)$$

where $f^*: H^n(W;\pi_n(W)) \to H^n(Y;\pi_n(W))$ *is the homomorphism induced by* f, *and* $\delta^*: H^n(Y;\pi_n(W)) \to H^{n+1}(X,Y;\pi_n(W))$ *is the coboundary homomorphism of the cohomology sequence of* (X,Y).

PROOF. Let $g:(X,X^n) \to (\hat{W},W)$ be an extension of f. Let $\Pi = \pi_n(W)$. The diagram

$$\begin{array}{ccccc}
H^n(W;\Pi) & \xrightarrow{f^*} & H^n(Y;\Pi) & \searrow^{\delta^*} & \\
\downarrow{\scriptstyle \delta^*} & & \downarrow{\scriptstyle \delta^*} & & \\
H^{n+1}(\hat{W},W;\Pi) & \xrightarrow{g^*} & H^{n+1}(X,X^n;\Pi) & \xrightarrow{i^*} & H^{n+1}(X,Y;\Pi) \\
& \searrow^{g^*} & \downarrow{\scriptstyle j^*} & & \\
& & H^{n+1}(X^{n+1},X^n;\Pi) = C^{n+1}(X,Y;\Pi) & &
\end{array}$$

is commutative, and j^* is an isomorphism of $H^{n+1}(X,X^n;\Pi)$ onto $Z^{n+1}(X,Y;\Pi)$. The homomorphism

$$i^* \circ j^{*-1}: Z^{n+1}(X,Y;\Pi) \to H^{n+1}(X,Y;\Pi)$$

is the natural homomorphism of the group of cocycles onto the cohomology group. Hence it suffices to show that

$$(*) \qquad g^*\delta^*\delta^n(W) = c_{f_1}^{n+1}$$

where $f_1 = g|X^n$. For then

$$\begin{aligned}
\delta^* f^* \delta^n(W) &= i^*\delta^* f^* \delta^n(W) \\
&= i^* g^* \delta^* \delta^n(W) \\
&= i^* j^{*-1} j^* g^* \delta^* \delta^n(W) \\
&= i^* j^{*-1} g^* \delta^* \delta^n(W) \\
&= i^* j^{*-1}(c_{f_1}^{n+1}) = \gamma^{n+1}(f)
\end{aligned}$$

To prove (*), consider the commutative diagram

$$(**) \qquad \begin{array}{ccccc}
\pi_{n+1}^*(X^{n+1},X^n) & \xrightarrow{g_*} & \pi_{n+1}(\hat{W},W) & \xrightarrow{\partial_*} & \pi_n(W) \\
\downarrow{\scriptstyle \rho} & & \downarrow{\scriptstyle \rho} & & \downarrow{\scriptstyle \rho} \\
H_{n+1}(X^{n+1},X^n) & \xrightarrow{g_*} & H_{n+1}(\hat{W},W) & \xrightarrow{\partial_*} & H_n(W)
\end{array}$$

This gives rise to a commutative diagram

$$\begin{array}{ccccc}
\text{Hom}\,\{\pi_{n+1}^*(X^{n+1},X^n),\Pi\} & \xleftarrow{g'} & \text{Hom}\,\{\pi_{n+1}(\hat{W},W),\Pi\} & \xleftarrow{\partial'} & \text{Hom}\,\{\pi_n(W),\Pi\} \\
\uparrow{\scriptstyle \rho'} & & \uparrow{\scriptstyle \rho'} & & \uparrow{\scriptstyle \rho'} \\
\text{Hom}\,\{H_{n+1}(X^{n+1},X^n),\Pi\} & \xleftarrow{g'} & \text{Hom}\,\{H_{n+1}(\hat{W},W),\Pi\} & \xleftarrow{\partial'} & \text{Hom}\,\{H_n(W),\Pi\} \\
|{\scriptstyle \theta} & & |{\scriptstyle \theta} & & |{\scriptstyle \theta} \\
H^{n+1}(X^{n+1},X^n;\Pi) & \overset{g^*}{-} & H^{n+1}(\hat{W},W;\Pi) & \overset{\delta^*}{-} & H^n(W;\Pi)
\end{array}$$

where the two top lines are obtained by duality from the diagram (**) (e.g., if $\eta \in \text{Hom}\,\{H_n(W),\Pi\}$, then $\rho'(\eta) = \eta \circ \rho$, etc.), and the homomorphisms denoted by "θ" are the isomorphisms onto of Lemma 8.8. The commutativity around the bottom squares of the diagram is easily checked.

Now $\theta(\delta^n(W)) = \rho^{-1}$ by definition of $\delta^n(W)$, and therefore

$$\begin{aligned} g'\partial'\rho'\theta(\delta^n(W)) &= g'\partial'\rho'(\rho^{-1}) \\ &= g'\partial'(\rho^{-1} \circ \rho) \\ &= g'(\rho^{-1} \circ \rho \circ \partial_*) \\ &= \rho^{-1} \circ \rho \circ \partial_* \circ g_* = \partial_* \circ g_* \end{aligned}$$

On the other hand, $\theta(c_{f_1}^{n+1}) = \partial_* \circ g_* \circ \rho^{-1}$ by definition of $c_{f_1}^{n+1}$; hence

$$\begin{aligned} \rho'\theta(c_{f_1}^{n+1}) &= \rho'(\partial_* \circ g_* \circ \rho^{-1}) = \partial_* \circ g_* \circ \rho^{-1} \circ \rho = \partial_* \circ g_* \\ &= g'\partial'\rho'\theta(\delta^n(W)) \\ &= \rho'\theta g^*\delta^*(\delta^n(W)) \end{aligned}$$

But $\rho' \circ \theta$ is an isomorphism onto. Hence

$$c_{f_1}^{n+1} = g^*\delta^*\delta^n(W) \qquad \text{Q.E.D.}$$

COROLLARY 2.8.9. *Let (X,Y) be a relative* CW *complex, W an $(n-1)$-connected n-simple space, and $f\colon Y \to W$ a map. Suppose that W is q-simple and that $H^{q+1}(X,Y;\pi_q(W)) = 0$ for $n+1 \leq q <$ dim (X,Y). Let $i^*\colon H^n(X;\pi_n(W)) \to H^n(Y;\pi_n(W))$ be the homomorphism induced by the inclusion map i. Then f has an extension to a map of X into W if and only if there is a homomorphism $\gamma\colon H^n(W;\pi_n(W)) \to H^n(X;\pi_n(W))$ such that $i^* \circ \gamma = f^*$.*

PROOF. If g is an extension of f, then $f = g \circ i$ and therefore $f^* = i^* \circ g^*$; we take $\gamma = g^*$. Conversely, suppose that such a γ exists. Then

$$\gamma^{n+1}(f) = \delta^*f^*\delta^n(W) = \delta^*i^*\gamma(\delta^n(W)) = 0$$

since δ^* and i^* are consecutive homomorphisms of the cohomology sequence of (X,Y). Q.E.D.

It is a simple matter to verify that when $Y = \emptyset$ and f is the constant map from X into W, then $\delta^n(g,f) = g^*\delta^n(W)$. Hence we may obtain two theorems that bear the same relationship to the homotopy and classification theorem, respectively, that Corollary 2.8.9 bears to the extension theorem.

COROLLARY 2.8.10. *Let X be a* CW *complex, W an $(n-1)$-connected n-simple space. Suppose that W is q-simple and that $H^q(X;\pi_q(W)) = 0$*

for $n + 1 \leq q \leq 1 + \dim x$. *Let* $f,g\colon X \to W$ *be maps. Then* f *and* g *are homotopic if and only if* $f^*\delta^n(W) = g^*\delta^n(W)$.

COROLLARY 2.8.11. *The correspondence* ϕ *of the classification theorem may be given by* $\phi(g) = g^*\delta^n(W)$.

NOTE. We have formulated Corollaries 2.8.10 and 2.8.11 only in the absolute case. For the relative case, we would need a new operation $(f - g)^*\colon H^n(W;G) \to H^n(X,Y;G)$ defined for any pair (X,Y), space W, and maps $f,g\colon X \to W$ such that $f|Y = g|Y$. However, we shall not take the time to do this.

PROBLEM 11. Let X be a 0-connected CW complex, W a 0-connected space. Suppose that $\pi_i(W) = 0$ for all $i > 1$. Then the homotopy classes of maps of X into W are in 1:1 correspondence with the conjugacy classes of homomorphisms of $\pi_1(X,x_0)$ into $\pi_1(W,w_0)$. [If G,H are groups, two homomorphisms $\phi,\psi\colon G \to H$ are said to be conjugate if and only if $\exists\, \beta \in H$ such that $\psi(\alpha) = \beta\phi(\alpha)\beta^{-1}$ for all $\alpha \in G$.] See, for instance, Hurewicz [14 (1936).]

2.9 Certain Identification Spaces

Let X,Y be spaces, A a closed subset of X, and $f\colon A \to Y$ a map. Assume that $X \cap Y = \emptyset$, and topologize $X \cup Y$ by defining a set $U \subset X \cup Y$ to be open if and only if $U \cap X$ and $U \cap Y$ are open in X and Y, respectively. Let $X \cup_f Y$ be the space obtained from $X \cup Y$ by identifying each $a \in A$ with $f(a) \in Y$; let $J\colon X \cup Y \to X \cup_f Y$ be the identification map. Then

1. J maps Y homeomorphically onto $J(Y)$.
2. J maps $X - A$ homeomorphically onto $J(X - A) = X \cup_f Y - J(Y)$.

For J is continuous and $J|Y$ and $J|X - A$ are 1:1. Let U be an open subset of $X - A$; then U is open in X and $\therefore$ in $X \cup Y$ and $J^{-1}J(U) = U$, whence $J(U)$ is open in $X \cup_f Y$ and $\therefore$ in $J(X - A)$. Hence Part 2 holds. Finally let U be an open subset of Y; since f is continuous, $f^{-1}(U)$ is open in A, and $\therefore$ $f^{-1}(U) = V \cap A$, where V is open in X. Let $U_1 = J(U \cup V)$. Then $J^{-1}(U_1) = U \cup V$, which is open in $X \cup Y$ and $\therefore$ U_1 is open in $X \cup_f Y$. But $U_1 \cap J(Y) = J(U)$, and therefore $J(U)$ is open in $J(Y)$. Hence Part 1 holds.

Because of Parts 1 and 2 we may assume that $X - A$ and Y are subspaces of $X \underset{f}{\cup} Y$, so that $X \underset{f}{\cup} Y = (X - A) \cup Y$. We henceforth make this assumption.

EXAMPLE 2.9.1. Let $y_0 \in Y$ and let $A \subset \pi_n(Y,y_0)$. For each $\alpha \in A$, let $f_\alpha:(I^{n+1},s_0) \to (Y,y_0)$ be a map representing α. Let $E = I^{n+1} \times A$; we make E into a space by assigning A the discrete topology. Let $S = \dot{I}^{n+1} \times A$, and define $f:S \to Y$ by $f(s,\alpha) = f_\alpha(s)$ for $s \in \dot{I}^{n+1}$, $\alpha \in A$. Let $Y^* = E \underset{f}{\cup} Y$. We assert that (Y^*,Y) is a relative CW complex. For let $E_\alpha^{n+1} = J(I^{n+1} \times \{\alpha\})$ and define $f_\alpha^{n+1}:(I^{n+1},\dot{I}^{n+1}) \to (Y^*,Y)$ by $f_\alpha^{n+1}(s) = J(s,\alpha)$. Then the E_α^{n+1} give a CW decomposition of (Y^*,Y) with characteristic maps f_α^{n+1}.

EXAMPLE 2.9.2. Let X,Y be spaces, $f:X \to Y$ a map. Let $X_1 = 1 \times X \subset I \times X$ and let $f_1:X_1 \to Y$ be defined by $f_1(1,x) = f(x)$. Let $C(f) = (I \times X) \underset{f_1}{\cup} Y$; $C(f)$ is called the *mapping cylinder* of f.

Define $i:X \to C(f)$, $j: Y \to C(f)$, $\pi:C(f) \to Y$ by

$$i(x) = J(0,x)$$
$$j(y) = J(y)$$
$$\begin{cases} \pi J(t,x) = f(x) \\ \pi J(y) \quad = y \end{cases}$$

Also define $F:I \times C(f) \to C(f)$ by

$$F(t,J(u,x)) = J(t + u - tu,x)$$
$$F(t,J(y)) = J(y)$$

We readily verify that F is well defined. Furthermore

$$\begin{cases} F(0,w) \quad = w \qquad (w \in C(f)) \\ F(1,w) \quad = j\pi(W) \\ F(t,j(y)) = j(y) \end{cases}$$

Thus F is a retraction by deformation of $C(f)$ onto $j(Y)$.

Consider the following diagram:

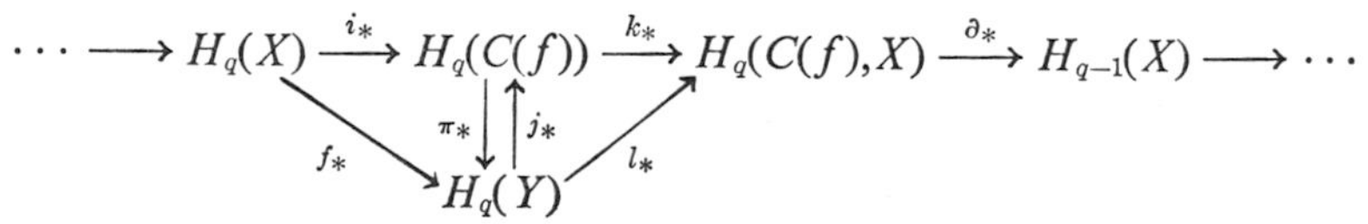
$\cdots \longrightarrow H_q(X) \xrightarrow{i_*} H_q(C(f)) \xrightarrow{k_*} H_q(C(f),X) \xrightarrow{\partial_*} H_{q-1}(X) \longrightarrow \cdots$
f_*
π_*
j_*
l_*
$H_q(Y)$

The homomorphisms k_* and l_* are induced by inclusion maps. Now $j \circ \pi$ is homotopic (under F) to the identity, and $\pi \circ j$ is the identity. Thus j_* is an isomorphism onto and $\pi_* = j_*^{-1}$. Also $\pi \circ i = f$, $k \circ j = l$.

Hence the foregoing diagram is commutative. Therefore the sequence

$$\cdots \to H_q(X) \xrightarrow{f_*} H_q(Y) \xrightarrow{l_*} H_q(C(f),X) \xrightarrow{\partial_*} H_{q-1}(X) \to \cdots$$

is exact. It is called the *homology sequence of the map f.*

Let $x_0 \in X$, $y_0 = f(x_0)$. Consider the diagram

$$\begin{array}{ccccccccc} \cdots \longrightarrow & \pi_q(X,x_0) & \xrightarrow{i_*} & \pi_q(C(f),x_0) & \xrightarrow{k_*} & \pi_q(C(f),X,x_0) & \longrightarrow & \pi_{q-1}(X,x_0) & \longrightarrow \cdots \\ & & {\scriptstyle f_*}\searrow & {\scriptstyle \pi_*}\downarrow\uparrow{\scriptstyle j'_*} & \nearrow{\scriptstyle l'_*} & & & & \\ & & & \pi_q(Y,y_0) & & & & & \end{array}$$

where $j'_* = \theta_\xi \circ j_*$, $j_*:\pi_q(Y,y_0) \to \pi_q(C(f),y_0)$ is induced by the inclusion map, $\xi \in \pi_1(C(f),y_0,x_0)$ is the homotopy class of the path p defined by

$$p(t) = J(1 - t,x_0)$$

and $l'_* = k_* \circ j'_*$. Then it may be proved in a manner similar to the foregoing that the sequence

$$\cdots \to \pi_q(X,x_0) \xrightarrow{f_*} \pi_q(Y,y_0) \xrightarrow{l'_*} \pi_q(C(f),X,x_0) \xrightarrow{\partial_*} \pi_{q-1}(X,x_0) \to \cdots$$

is exact. It is called the *homotopy sequence of the map f.*

2.10 Eilenberg-MacLane Spaces [5, 23]

DEFINITION. *Let* Π *be a group and n an integer* ≥ 1 (Π *abelian if* $n > 1$). *An Eilenberg-MacLane space of type* (Π,n) *is a space X such that* $\pi_i(X) = 0$ *for* $i \neq n$, $\pi_n(X) \approx \Pi$.

The importance of these spaces is shown by the classification theorem of the last section: If W is an Eilenberg-MacLane space of type (Π,n) and Π is abelian, then for any CW complex X, the group $H^n(X;\Pi)$ is in 1:1 correspondence with the set of homotopy classes of X into W.

We now prove a theorem from which we deduce the existence of Eilenberg-MacLane space with given (Π,n).

THEOREM 2.10.1. *Let X be a* 0*-connected space, n an integer* ≥ 1, *and let R be a subgroup of* $\pi_n(X,x_0)$, *closed under the operations of* $\pi_1(X,x_0)$. *Then there is a relative* CW *complex* (X^*,X) *such that, if* $i: X \subset X^*$, *then*

1. $i_*:\pi_r(X) \approx \pi_r(X^*)$ $\quad (r < n)$.
2. $i_*:\pi_n(X) \to \pi_n(X^*)$ *is onto and has kernel R.*
3. $\pi_i(X^*) = 0$ $\quad$ *for* $i > n$.

PROOF. We construct X^* by constructing inductively the skeleta X^{*r}. Define $X^{*0} = X^{*1} = \cdots = X^{*n} = X$. Suppose that X^{*r} has been constructed $(r \geq n)$. Let A be a set of generators (over $\pi_1(X^{*r},x_0)$) of

$$\left\{\begin{matrix} R \text{ if } r = n \\ \pi_r(X^{*r},x_0) \text{ if } r > n \end{matrix}\right\} \text{ (i.e., the group } \left\{\begin{matrix} R \\ \pi_r(X^{*r},x_0) \end{matrix}\right\}$$

is generated by the elements $\theta_\xi(\alpha)$ with $\alpha \in A$, $\xi \in \pi_1(X^{*r},x_0)$. Define X^{*r+1} to be the Y^* of Example 2.9.1 with $Y = X^{*r}$. Let $X^* = \bigcup_{r=0}^{\infty} X^{*r}$; a subset $U \subset X^*$ is said to be closed if and only if $U \cap X^{*r}$ is closed in X^{*r} for all r. Then it is readily verified that (X^*,X) is a relative CW complex with cells E^{r+1} and characteristic maps f_α^{r+1}.

Now (X^{*r+1},X^{*r}) is r-connected; hence the sequence

$$\pi_{r+1}(X^{*r+1},X^{*r}) \xrightarrow{\partial_*} \pi_r(X^{*r}) \xrightarrow{i_*} \pi_r(X^{*r+1}) \to 0$$

is exact. If $r < n$, then $X^{*r+1} = X^{*r}$, and therefore

$$i_*:\pi_r(X^{*r}) \approx \pi_r(X^{*r+1}) \qquad (r < n)$$

Suppose that $r \geq n$. Let γ_α^{r+1} be the element of $\pi_{r+1}(X^{*r+1},X^{*r})$ represented by f_α^{r+1}; then $\partial_*\gamma_\alpha^{r+1} = \alpha$. Now $\pi_{r+1}(X^{*r+1},X^{*r})$ is generated by the elements $\bar{\theta}_\xi(\gamma_\alpha^{r+1})$ with $\alpha \in A$, $\xi \in \pi_1(X^{*r})$. Hence Kernel $i_* =$ Image ∂_* is generated by the elements $\theta_\xi(\alpha)$ with $\xi \in \pi_1(X^{*r})$.

Thus

$$\text{Kernel } i_* = \left\{\begin{matrix} R & \text{if } r = n \\ \pi_r(X^{*r}) & \text{if } r > n \end{matrix}\right\}$$

Hence

$$\left\{\begin{matrix} i_*:\pi_n(X^{*n}) \to \pi_n(X^{*n+1}) \text{ is onto and has kernel } R \\ \pi_n(X^{*r+1}) = 0 \qquad \text{if } r > n \end{matrix}\right.$$

But $\pi_r(X^{*r+1}) \approx \pi_r(X^*)$ under the inclusion map. Since $X^{*r} = X$ for $r \leq n$, the desired conclusion follows immediately.

COROLLARY 2.10.2. *Let* Π *be a group, n an integer* ≥ 1 *(if* $n > 1$, *assume that* Π *is abelian). Then there is a* CW *complex* X^* *which is an Eilenberg-MacLane space of type* (Π,n).

PROOF. Let $\phi:F \to \Pi$ be a homomorphism onto, where

$$F \text{ is a } \left\{\begin{matrix} \text{free group if } n = 1 \\ \text{free abelian group if } n > 1 \end{matrix}\right\}$$

and let B be a set of free generators of F. Let X be the space obtained from $I^n \times B$ (B topologized discretely) by identifying all the points (s,β) with $s \in \dot{I}^n$, $\beta \in B$ to a single point x_0; X is the union of a family of n-spheres $S_\beta^n = j(I^n \times \{\beta\})$, and $S_{\beta_1}^n \cap S_{\beta_2}^n = \{x_0\}$ if $\beta_1 \neq \beta_2$. Clearly X is a CW complex with cells S_β^n and characteristic maps $f_\beta^n:f_\beta^n(s) = j(s,\beta)$ for $s \in I^n$, $\beta \in B$; $X^0 = \cdots = X^{n-1} = \{x_0\}$, $X^n = X$. Then the map which sends β into the element γ_β^n of $\pi_n(X,x_0)$ represented by ϕ_β^n

induces an isomorphism σ of F onto $\pi_n(X,x_0)$. If $n = 1$ this follows from Seifert and Threlfall [B.4, Chapter 7]. If $n > 1$, then $X^1 = x_0$; therefore X is 1-connected and $\rho:\pi_n(X) \approx H_n(X)$. But $\beta \to e_\beta^n$ induces an isomorphism σ' of F onto $H_n(X)$, and $\rho(\gamma_\beta^n) = e_\beta^n$. Thus $\sigma = \rho^{-1} \circ \sigma'$ is an isomorphism onto.

THEOREM 2.10.3. *Let X,Y be 0-connected spaces, $f:X \to Y$ a map, $N \geq 1$. If $f_*:\pi_n(X) \approx \pi_n(Y)$ for $n \leq N$, then $f_*:H_n(X) \approx H_n(Y)$ for $n \leq N - 1$, and $f_*:H_N(X) \twoheadrightarrow H_N(Y)$. Conversely, suppose that X and Y are 1-connected and $f_*:H_n(X) \approx H_n(Y)$ for $n \leq N$. Then $f_*:\pi_n(X) \approx \pi_n(Y)$ for $n \leq N - 1$ and $f_*:\pi_N(X) \twoheadrightarrow \pi_N(Y)$.* *

PROOF. Let $C(f)$ be the mapping cylinder of f. If $f_*:\pi_n(X) \approx \pi_n(Y)$ for $n \leq N$, then $\pi_n(C(f),X) = 0$ for $n \leq N$. Hence, by the Hurewicz theorem, $H_n(C(f),X) = 0$ for $n \leq N$, and the first statement of the theorem follows. Conversely, suppose that X and Y are 1-connected, and that $f_*:H_n(X) \approx H_n(Y)$ for $n \leq N$. It follows that $H_n(C(f),X) = 0$ for $n \leq N$. Since Y is 1-connected, $C(f)$ is 1-connected and hence $(C(f),X)$ is 1-connected. Suppose that $\pi_i(C(f),X) = 0$ for all $i < n \leq N$. Now X is 1-connected and therefore $\pi_1(X)$ operates trivially on $\pi_n(C(f),X)$. Hence $\rho:\pi_n(C(f),X) \approx H_n(C(f),X) = 0$. Hence by induction $\pi_n(C(f),X) = 0$ for all $n \leq N$. The statement of the converse follows at once.

THEOREM 2.10.4. *Let X be an Eilenberg-MacLane* CW *complex, Y an Eilenberg-MacLane space, both of type* (Π,n). *Then there is a map $f:X \to Y$ such that $f_*:\pi_n(X) \approx \pi_n(Y)$.*

PROOF. We have seen that the homotopy classes of maps of X into Y are in 1:1 correspondence with the elements of $H^n(X;\pi_n(Y))$. Since X is also $(n - 1)$-connected, the latter group is isomorphic with Hom $\{H_n(X),\pi_n(Y)\}$. Choose an isomorphism $\phi:\pi_n(X) \approx \pi_n(Y)$, and let $u \in H^n(X;\pi_n(Y))$ be the element which corresponds to

$$\phi \circ \rho^{-1}:H_n(X) \to \pi_n(Y)$$

Let $f:X \to Y$ be a map such that $f^*\delta^n(Y) = u$. Then we assert that $f_* = \phi:\pi_n(X) \approx \pi_n(Y)$. In fact, the diagram

$$\begin{array}{ccc}
H^n(X;\pi_n(Y)) & \xleftarrow{f^*} & H^n(Y;\pi_n(Y)) \\
\downarrow \theta & & \downarrow \theta \\
\text{Hom}\,\{H_n(X),\pi_n(Y)\} & \xleftarrow{g} & \text{Hom}\,\{H_n(Y),\pi_n(Y)\}
\end{array}$$

is commutative, where the θ's are the natural isomorphisms onto of Lemma 8.8 and $g(\eta) = \eta \circ f_*$. Now, by definition, $\delta^n(Y) = \theta^{-1}(\rho^{-1})$ and

* The statement $f:P \twoheadrightarrow Q$ means that f maps P *onto* Q, while $f:P \twoheadrightarrow Q$ means that f is a $1:L$ map of P into Q.

therefore $f^*\delta^n(Y) = f^*\theta^{-1}(\rho^{-1}) = \theta^{-1}(g(\rho^{-1})) = \theta^{-1}(\rho^{-1} \circ f_*)$. But, by the construction of f, $f^*\delta^n(Y) = u = \theta^{-1}(\phi \circ \rho^{-1})$ and therefore

$$\phi \circ \rho^{-1} = \rho^{-1} \circ f_*$$

Hence $f_*: H_n(X) \to H_n(Y)$ is equal to $\rho \circ \phi \circ \rho^{-1}$. But the diagram

$$\begin{array}{ccc} \pi_n(X) & \xrightarrow{f_*} & \pi_n(Y) \\ \downarrow{\scriptstyle \rho} & & \downarrow{\scriptstyle \rho} \\ H_n(X) & \xrightarrow{f_*} & H_n(Y) \end{array}$$

is commutative, and it follows that $f_* = \pi_n(X) \to \pi_n(Y)$ is equal to ϕ.

COROLLARY 2.10.5. *Let X,Y be Eilenberg-MacLane spaces of type* (Π,n). *Then $H_q(X) \approx H_q(Y)$ for all q.*

For let W be an Eilenberg-MacLane CW complex of type (Π,n). Then $\exists$ maps $f: W \to X$, $g: W \to Y$ such that $f_*:\pi_n(W) \approx \pi_n(X)$, $g_*:\pi_n(W) \approx \pi_n(Y)$. Then $f_*:\pi_q(W) \approx \pi_q(X)$ and $g_*:\pi_q(W) \approx \pi_q(Y)$ for all q, and therefore $f_*:H_q(W) \approx H_q(X)$, $g_*:H_q(W) \approx H_q(Y)$ for all q. Hence

$$g_* \circ f_*^{-1}: H_q(X) \approx H_q(Y)$$

for all q.

(We have assumed $n > 1$ here; if $n = 1$, the result follows from Problem 9.)

Thus the homology groups of an Eilenberg-MacLane space of type (Π,n) depend only on (Π,n); we denote them by $H_q(\Pi,n)$.

REMARK 2.10.6.* *Under the hypotheses of Theorem* 2.10.3, *if $f_*:\pi_n(X) \approx \pi_n(Y)$ for $n \leq N$, then*

$$\begin{array}{ll} f_*: H_n(X;G) \approx H_N(Y;G) & n \leq N-1 \\ f_*: H_n(X;G) \twoheadrightarrow H_N(Y;G) & \\ f^*: H^n(Y;G) \approx H^n(X;G) & n \leq N-1 \\ f^*: H^N(Y;G) \rightarrowtail H^N(X;G) & \end{array}$$

PROOF. This follows from the universal coefficient theorem, for

$$\begin{array}{ll} H_n(C(f),X) = 0 & n \leq N \\ \Rightarrow \begin{cases} H_n(C(f),X;G) = 0 \\ H^n(C(f),X;G) = 0 \end{cases} & \begin{array}{l} n \leq N \\ n \leq N \end{array} \end{array}$$

From Remark 2.10.6 and Theorem 2.10.4 we have the following Corollary.

COROLLARY 2.10.7. *If X and Y are Eilenberg-MacLane spaces of type* (Π,n), *then*

$$H^q(X;G) \approx H^q(Y;G) \quad \text{and} \quad H_q(X;G) \approx H_q(Y;G)$$

* See footnote previous page.

Eilenberg and MacLane, in the paper in which these spaces were first investigated [5, p. 480], exhibited for each pair (Π,n) an abstract chain complex $K(\Pi,n)$ and for each space X a chain map $\alpha:C^{n-1}(X) \to K(\pi_n(X),n)$ which they proved is a chain equivalence if X is an Eilenberg-MacLane space of type $(\pi_n(X),n)$.

NOTE. The statements corresponding in the relative case to those of Theorem 2.10.3 are both false.

I. If $f:(X,A) \to (Y,B)$ induces an isomorphism onto $f_*:\pi_n(X,A) \approx \pi_n(Y,B)$ for all n, then it does not follow that the induced homomorphisms $f_*:H_n(X,A) \to H_n(Y,B)$ are all isomorphisms onto as well. For a counterexample,* let $X = S^{2k+1}$, $Y = P^k(C)$, where C is the field of complex numbers, f the usual fibre-mapping, B a point in Y, and A the fibre $f^{-1}(B)$. The counterexample works for any $k \geq 2$; for by 3.2.1,

$$f_*:\pi_n(X,A) \approx \pi_n(Y,B) \text{ for all } n$$

On the other hand, since $H_{2k}(X) = 0$ and $H_{2k-1}(A) = 0$, it follows from the exact sequence that $H_{2k}(X,A) = 0$, while $H_2(Y,B) \approx H_{2k}(Y) = H_{2k}(P^k(C)) = Z$. [See for instance Seifert and Threlfall, B.4, bottom of p. 318.]

II. If $f:(X,A) \to (Y,B)$ induces an isomorphism onto $f_*:H_n(X,A) \approx H_n(Y,B)$ for every n, then it does not follow that the induced homomorphisms $f_*:\pi_n(X,A) \to \pi_n(Y,B)$ are all isomorphisms onto as well. For a counterexample,* let Y be the unit sphere in 3-space, B the subspace of Y all of whose points have nonnegative z coordinates, X the subspace of Y all of whose points have nonpositive z coordinates, $A = X \cap B$, and f the inclusion map. Then A is a circle and f induces an excision; hence $f_*:H_n(X,A) \approx H_n(Y,B)$ for all n. On the other hand, $\pi_3(X,A) \approx \pi_2(A) = \pi_2(R^1) = 0$ since R^1 is contractible and covers the circle; and $\pi_3(Y,B) \approx \pi_3(Y) = \pi_3(S^2)$. By Section 1 of the next chapter, S^3 is a fibre space over S^2 with fibre S^1; hence by Corollary 3.2.3, we have that the sequence

$$0 = \pi_3(S^1) \to \pi_3(S^3) \to \pi_3(S^2) \to \pi_2(S^1) = \pi_2(R^1) = 0$$

is exact; hence $\pi_3(S^2) \approx \pi_3(S^3) = Z$.

III. It is important to note that Theorem 2.10.3 holds only if there exists a map f which induces the isomorphism involved. Thus, it is possible to find spaces X and Y such that $\pi_n(X) \approx \pi_n(Y)$ for all n but for which there exist n for which $H_n(X) \not\approx H_n(Y)$. For instance, let $X = P^m(R) \times S^n$, $Y = S^m \times P^n(R)$, $m,n > 1$. ($P^n(R)$ is n-dimensional real projective space, obtained from S^n by identifying "opposite" points. Clearly S^n is a 2-sheeted universal covering space of $P^n(R)$.) Then $\pi_1(X) \approx \pi_1(P^m(R)) \oplus \pi_1(S^n) \approx \pi_1(P^m(R)) \approx Z_2$ by Remark 3.2.5.

Similarly $\pi_1(Y) \approx Z_2$, and hence $\pi_1(X) \approx \pi_1(Y)$. If $k > 1$, then $\pi_k(P^m(R)) = \pi_k(S^m)$, and hence $\pi_k(X) \approx \pi_k(P^m(R)) \oplus \pi_k(S^n) \approx \pi_k(S^m) \oplus \pi_k(S^n) \approx \pi_k(S^n) \oplus \pi_k(S^m) \approx \pi_k(P^n(R)) \oplus \pi_k(S^m) = \pi_k(Y)$. On the other hand, if we let $m > n$, then we have by the Künneth formula*

$$H_m(P^m(R) \times S^n) \approx \sum_{p=0}^{m} H_p(P^m(R)) \otimes H_{m-p}(S^n) \oplus \sum_{p=0}^{m} H_p(P^m(R)) * H_{m-p-1}(S^n)$$

Since the homology of S^n has no torsion, the second summand vanishes, and the only nonvanishing terms of the first summand are $p = m - n$ and $p = m$, in which cases $H_{m-p}(S^n) = Z$. Hence

$$H_m(P^m(R) \times S^n) \approx H_{m-n}(P^m(R)) \oplus H_m(P^m(R))$$

Similarly

$$H_m(S^m \times P^n(R)) \approx H_0(P^n(R)) \oplus H_m(P^n(R)) \approx H_0(P^n(R)) = Z$$

This can agree with the former group only if m and n are both odd (Seifert and Threlfall, B.4, p. 119), so that choosing one of them even yields the counterexample.

IV. The converse is also false. That is to say, there exist spaces X and Y such that $H_n(X) \approx H_n(Y)$ for all n but there is an n for which $\pi_n(X) \not\approx \pi_n(Y)$. For instance,* let $X = S_k^4 \times S^2$, $Y = P^3(C)$. Then

$$H_k(X) \approx \sum_{p=0}^{k} H_p(S^2) \otimes H_{k-p}(S^4)$$

since S^2 has no torsion. If k is odd or >6, this is clearly 0. If $k = 6$, we have $H_k(X) \approx H_2(S^2) \otimes H_4(S^4) \approx Z \otimes Z \approx Z$. If $k = 4$, we have

$$H_k(X) \approx H_0(S^2) \otimes H_4(S^4) \approx Z$$

Similarly $H_0(X) \approx H_2(X) \approx Z$. By Seifert and Threlfall, [B.4] bottom of p. 318, this agrees with the homology of $P^3(C)$. On the other hand, by Remark 3.2.5, $\pi_4(Y) = \pi_4(P^3(C)) = \pi_4(S^7) = 0$, while

$$\pi_4(X) = \pi_4(S^2 \times S^4) = \pi_4(S^2) \oplus \pi_4(S^4)$$

which contains $Z = \pi_4(S^4)$ as a subgroup and so is not zero.

Another example is as follows. Denote by $S^2 \vee S^4$ the union of S^2 and S^4 with one point identified. More formally, if we let $a \in S^2$, $b \in S^4$, then $S^2 \vee S^4$ is the subset of $S^2 \times S^4$ defined by $S^2 \times b \cup a \times S^4$; the only point in common in (a,b). Let $X = S^2 \vee S^4$, $Y = P^2(C)$. Then by the Mayer-Vietoris theorem $H_k(X) = H_k(S^2) \oplus H_k(S^4)$, and

* This counterexample depends on Sections 3.1 and 3.2.

this clearly agrees with the homology of $P^2(C)$ (Seifert and Threlfall, B.4, bottom of p. 318). On the other hand, $\pi_4(Y) = \pi_4(P^2(C)) = \pi_4(S^5) = 0$ by 3.2.5. Now $a \times S^4$ is a retraction of $S^2 \vee S^4$ under a retraction r which sends $S^2 \times b$ into (a,b). Furthermore if $i: a \times S^4 \to S^2 \vee S^4$ is the inclusion, then $r \circ i =$ identity. Hence $r_* \circ i_*: \pi_4(a \times S^4) \to \pi_4(a \times S^4)$ is the identity as well. But image $i_* \subset \pi_4(S^2 \vee S^4)$. If this were to vanish, it would mean that image $r_* \circ i_* = \pi_4(a \times S^4) \approx \pi_4(S^4) \approx Z$ would vanish also, which is absurd. Hence

$$\pi_4(X) = \pi_4(S^2 \vee S^4) \neq 0$$

REMARK 2.10.8. *The Künneth formula holds for Eilenberg-MacLane spaces in the sense that if* Π_1, Π_2 *are arbitrary groups, abelian for* $n > 1$, *then*

$$H_q(\Pi_1 \oplus \Pi_2, n) \approx \sum_{p=0}^{q} H_p(\Pi_1, n) \otimes H_{q-p}(\Pi_2, n) \oplus \sum_{p} H_p(\Pi_1, n) * H_{q-p-1}(\Pi_2, n)$$

PROOF. Let X_1 be of type (Π_1, n), X_2 of type (Π_2, n). Then clearly $X_1 \times X_2$ is of type $(\Pi_1 \oplus \Pi_2, n)$, and the result follows from the ordinary Künneth formula.

REMARK 2.10.9. $H_q(Z,1) \approx \begin{cases} Z & q = 0,1 \\ 0 & \text{otherwise} \end{cases}$

PROOF. $\pi_1(S^1) \approx Z$, $\pi_k(S^1) \approx \pi_k(R^1) = 0$ for $k > 1$. Hence S^1 is an Eilenberg-MacLane space of type $(Z,1)$. The result follows at once.

THEOREM 2.10.10. $H_k(Z_m,1) \approx \begin{cases} Z & k = 0 \\ Z_m & k \text{ odd} \\ 0 & \text{otherwise} \end{cases}$

PROOF. We first construct an Eilenberg-MacLane space L of type $(Z_m,1)$, then calculate its homology groups. Let C^n be the set of all infinite sequences of complex numbers $(z_1, z_2, \cdots, z_n, \cdots)$ such that for $k > n$, $z_k = 0$. We define C^∞ by $C^\infty = \bigcup_{i=1}^{\infty} C^i$ and topologize it by stipulating that a set $A \subset C^\infty$ is closed if and only if $A \cap C^i$ is closed in the natural topology of C^i for every i. Let

$$S^\infty = \left\{ z \in C^\infty \,\middle|\, \sum_{i=1}^{\infty} |z_i|^2 = 1 \right\}$$

then

$$S^\infty = \bigcup_{n=1}^{\infty} \left\{ z \in C^n \middle| \sum_{i=1}^{n} |z_i|^2 = 1 \right\}$$
$$= \bigcup_{n=0}^{\infty} S^{2n+1} \qquad (S^{2n-1} \subset S^{2n+1} \qquad n = 1,\cdots)$$

the S^{2n+1}'s being homeomorphic images of the standard spheres of odd dimension. It follows that $\pi_k(S^\infty) = 0$ for $k > 0$; for let $f\colon S^k \to S^\infty$ be a map; then it is not hard to see from compactness considerations that $f(S^k) \subset S^{2n+1}$ for some n. We can clearly choose this $2n + 1$ to be as large as we please. In particular we can choose it so that it is larger than k. Then since $\pi_k(S^{2n+1}) = 0$, it follows that f is zero-homotopic in S^{2n+1}, so that *a fortiori* it is zero-homotopic in S^∞. This shows that $\pi_k(S^\infty) = 0$ for every k. Now let $\zeta = e^{2\pi i/m}$ and define $T\colon S^\infty \to S^\infty$ by

$$T((z_1,z_2,\cdots,z_n,\cdots)) = (z_1\zeta,z_2\zeta,\cdots,z_n\zeta,\cdots)$$

Let L be the identification space obtained from S^∞ by identifying any two points z^1 and z^2 in S^∞ for which $z^2 = T(z^1)$; let j be the identification map. Then clearly S^∞ is a covering space of L and in fact it is a universal covering space, since $\pi_1(S^\infty) = 0$. Hence $\pi_k(L) = 0$, $k > 1$. Furthermore, the covering translations of S^∞ over L are simply all the T^i. Since $T^m =$ identity, it follows that $\pi_1(L) = Z_m$. Hence L is an Eilenberg-MacLane space of type $(Z_m,1)$.

Now let

$E^{2k} = \{z \in S^\infty | z_i = 0$ for $i > k + 1$ and z_{k+1} is real and nonnegative$\}$

$E^{2k+1} = \{z \in S^\infty | z_i = 0$ for $i > k + 1$ and $0 \leq \arg z_{k+1} \leq 2\pi/m$ or $z_{k+1} = 0\}$. L is a CW complex with cells $F^i = j(E^i)$, $i = 0,1,2,\cdots$. Then clearly

$$\begin{cases} \partial F^{2i+1} = 0 \\ \partial F^{2i} \quad = mF^{2i-1} \end{cases}$$

All the $(2i + 1)$ chains of L are therefore of the form kF^{2i+1}. By the foregoing remark they are all cycles, and they bound if and only if $k = m$. Hence $H_{2i+1}(L) = Z_m$. Similarly all $2i$ chains of L are of the form kF^{2i}. But $\partial(kF^{2i}) = kmF^{2i-1}$, which is not zero unless k is. Hence there are no nonzero $2i$ cycles in L, and it follows that for $i > 0$, $H_{2i}(L) = 0$. Q.E.D.

3. Fibre Spaces

3.1 Definitions and Examples [15, 19]

We have seen that, if X is a space and $x_0 \in X$, then $\pi_n(X,x_0) \approx \pi_{n-1}(F^1(X,x_0),e_{x_0}) = \pi_{n-1}(X_1,x_1)$ where $x_1 = e_{x_0} = e^1_{x_0}$ and X_1 is the path component of x_1 in $F^1(X,x_0)$. If we define inductively a sequence $(X_0,x_0),\cdots,(X_n,x_n)$ by

$$\begin{cases} X_0 = X \\ X_{i+1} = \text{the component of } e_{x_i} \text{ in } F^1(X_i,x_i) \\ x_{i+1} = e_{x_i} \end{cases}$$

then we have $\pi_n(X,x_0) \approx \pi_{n-1}(X_1,x_1) \approx \cdots \approx \pi_1(X_{n-1},x_{n-1})$. Now if $n > 1$, X_{n-1} is an H-space and therefore $\pi_1(X_{n-1},x_{n-1})$ is abelian (Theorem 1.3.5), and hence $\pi_1(X_{n-1},x_{n-1}) \approx H_1(X_{n-1})$. Thus the problem of computing the homotopy groups of X is contained in the problem of computing the homology groups of the X_i. By induction, it suffices to know how to calculate the homology groups of X_1 from those of X.

Let $T(X,x_0)$ be the space of all paths in X which *start* at x_0, and define $\pi:T(X,x_0) \to X$ by $\pi(f) = f(1)$. Then π is continuous and $\pi^{-1}(x_0) = F^1(X,x_0)$.

THEOREM 3.1.1. *Let Y be a space, $f: Y \times I \to X$ a map, $g: Y \to T(X,x_0)$ a map such that $\pi(g(y)) = f(y,0)$; then there is a map $G: Y \times I \to T(X,x_0)$ such that $\pi \circ G = f$ and $G(y,0) = g(y)$.*

PROOF. Define a map $H:(Y \times I \times \dot{I}) \cup (Y \times 0 \times I) \to X$ by

$$\begin{cases} H(y,s,0) = x_0 \\ H(y,s,1) = f(y,s) \\ H(y,0,t) = g(y)(t) \end{cases}$$

Then H is continuous. Now $I \times \dot{I} \cup 0 \times I$ is a retract if $I \times \dot{I}$, and therefore $Y \times I \times \dot{I} \cup Y \times 0 \times I$ is a retract of $Y \times I \times I$; hence H has an extension $H_1: Y \times I \times I \to X$. Define $G: Y \times I \to T(X,x_0)$ by

$$G(y,s)(t) = H_1(y,s,t)$$

Then G is the desired map. The map G is called a *covering homotopy* of f, and Theorem 3.1.1 is referred to as the *covering homotopy theorem.*

DEFINITION. *Let X,B be spaces and $\pi: X \to B$ a map. We say that π is a* fibre map *and that X is a* fibre space *over B with respect to π if and only if for every compact polyhedron Y and maps $g: Y \to X$, $f: Y \times I \to B$, such that $\pi(g(y)) = f(y,0)$ for all $y \in Y$, there is a map $G: Y \times I \to X$ such that $G(y,0) = g(y)$ and $\pi(G(y,t)) = f(y,t)$ for all $y \in Y$, $t \in I$.*

If $\pi: X \to B$ is a fibre map and $b \in B$, the set $F_b = \pi^{-1}(b)$ is called the fibre over B.

Theorem 3.1.1 *asserts that, for any pair (X,x_0), the map $\pi: T(X,x_0) \to X$ is a fibre map; the fibre $\pi^{-1}(x_0)$ is $F^1(X,x_0)$.*

THEOREM 3.1.2. *Let B be a connected $lc^{1/2}$-space and (X,π) a covering of B. Then π is a fibre map.*

PROOF. Since B and Y are $lc^{1/2}$ and thus in particular locally connected, we may assume that Y is connected; otherwise we define G separately on each component of $Y \times I$. Let $y_0 \in Y$. Define $i: Y \to Y \times I$ by $i(y) = (y,0)$. Now $i(Y) = Y \times 0$ is a deformation retract of $Y \times I$ and therefore $i_*: \pi_1(Y,y_0) \approx \pi_1(Y \times I,(y_0,0))$. Hence

$$\begin{aligned} f_*\pi_1(Y \times I,(y_0,0)) &= f_*i_*\pi_1(Y,y_0) \\ &= \pi_*g_*\pi_1(Y,y_0) \\ &\subset \pi_*\pi_1(X,g(y_0)) \end{aligned}$$

Therefore, by the theory of covering spaces, there is a map $G: Y \times I \to X$ such that $G(y_0,0) = g(y_0)$ and $\pi \circ G = f$. Now if $y \in Y$, we have $\pi G(y,0) = f(y,0) = \pi g(y)$; since Y is connected, it follows that $G(y,0) = g(y)$ for all $y \in Y$. Then G satisfies the foregoing definition.

THEOREM 3.1.3. *Let $\pi: X \to B$ be a map. Let U be a neighborhood of the diagonal in $B \times B$, $U_1 = \{(x,b) \in X \times B | (\pi(x),b) \in U\}$. Suppose that $\exists$ a map $\phi: U_1 \to X$ such that*

$$\begin{cases}\phi(x,\pi(x)) = x & (x \in X) \\ \pi\phi(x,b) = b & ((x,b) \in U_1)\end{cases}$$

(Such a ϕ will be called a slicing function *for π.) Then π is a fibre map.*

PROOF. We first claim that $\exists\, \delta > 0$ such that, if $t',t'' \in I$, $|t' - t''| < \delta$, then for all $y \in Y$, $(f(y,t'),f(y,t'')) \in U$. For if not, there are sequences $\{y_n\}$, $\{t'_n\}$, $\{t''_n\}$ such that $y_n \in Y$, $t'_n,t''_n \in I$, $|t'_n - t''_n| < 1/n$, and $(f(y_n,t'_n),f(y_n,t''_n)) \notin U$. Since Y and I are compact, by passing to subsequences we may assume that $y_n \to y \in Y$, $t'_n \to t \in I$, and $t''_n \to t$. Let V be a neighborhood of $f(y,t)$ such that $V \times V \subset U$. Then, for n sufficiently large, we have $f(y_n,t'_n) \in V$, $f(y_n,t''_n) \in V$, and $\therefore$

$$(f(y_n,t'_n),f(y_n,t''_n)) \in U$$

a contradiction. Now let $0 = t_0 < t_1 < \cdots < t_n = 1$ be a partition of I with $t_{i+1} - t_i < \delta$, $(i = 0,1,\cdots,n-1)$. We define G inductively over the sets $\{(y,t)|t_i \leq t \leq t_{i+1}\}$. Let $G(y,0) = g(y)$. Assume that $G(y,t)$ has been defined for all (y,t) with $0 \leq t \leq t_i$ and that $\pi G(y,t) = f(y,t)$. Now if $t_i \leq t \leq t_{i+1}$, then $(f(y,t_i),f(y,t)) \in U$, and therefore $(G(y,t_i),f(y,t)) \in U_1$, so that $\phi(G(y,t_i),f(y,t))$ is defined. Now

$$\phi(G(y,t_i),f(y,t_i)) = G(y,t_i)$$
$$\pi\phi(G(y,t_i),f(y,t)) = f(y,t)$$

Hence we may extend the definition of G by defining

$$G(y,t) = \phi(G(y,t_i),f(y,t)), \qquad (y \in Y,\ t_i \leq t \leq t_{i+1})$$

THEOREM 3.1.4. *Let $\pi: X \to B$ be a map such that X is a fibre bundle over B with π as projection. Then π is a fibre map.*

For the covering homotopy theorem holds (Steenrod, [B.5], p. 54).

COROLLARY 3.1.5. *Let G be a connected Lie group, H a closed subgroup of G, K a closed subgroup of H, and $\pi: G/K \to G/H$ the natural map. Then π is a fibre map* [B.5, p. 33].

EXAMPLE. Let K be one of the s-fields $R = \{\text{reals}\}$, $C = \{\text{complex numbers}\}$, $Q = \{\text{quaternions}\}$, and let K^n be the Cartesian nth power of K, which we regard as a left vector space over K with the usual inner product. Let G be the unitary group of K^n; thus $G = O(n)$, $U(n)$, or $Sp(n)$. Let e_1 be a unit vector in K^n, and let $H = \{T \in G | Te_1 = \lambda e_1$ for some $\lambda \in K\}$ (necessarily $|\lambda| = 1$ since T is unitary), $H_0 = \{T \in G | Te_1 = e_1\}$. Thus $G \supset H \supset H_0$.

Let S be the unit sphere in K^n and define $\pi: G \to S$ by $\pi(T) = T(e_1)$.

Then $\pi(T_1) = \pi(T_2)$ if and only if $T_1^{-1}T_2 \in H_0$; thus π induces a 1:1 map

$$\bar{\pi}: G/H_0 \to S$$

It is easy to see that π is onto, and therefore that $\bar{\pi}$ is onto. Thus G/H^0 is homeomorphic with S.

Let $P = P^{n-1}(K)$ be the $(n-1)$-dimensional projective space over K; P is the space obtained from $K^n - \{0\}$ by identifying two points x and y if and only if $y = \lambda x$ for some $\lambda \in K$. Let $\eta: K^n - \{0\} \to P$ be the identification map. Define $\psi: G \to P$ by $\psi(T) = \eta(T(e_1))$. Then $\psi(T_1) = \psi(T_2)$ if and only if $T_1^{-1}T_2 \in H$, whence ψ induces a 1:1 map $\bar{\psi}: G/H \to P$. Again it is easy to see that ψ is onto and therefore $\bar{\psi}$ is onto. Thus G/H is homeomorphic with P.

Finally, define $\phi: H \to K$ by $\phi(T) = (Te_1)\cdot e_1 =$ the λ such that $Te_1 = \lambda e_1$. Then we see, in the same manner as above, that ϕ induces a homeomorphism of H/H_0 onto the unit sphere Σ in K.

If $K = R$, then $\Sigma = \{1,-1\} = S^0$ and $S = S^{n-1}$; if $K = C$, $\Sigma = S^1$ and $S = S^{2n-1}$; if $K = Q$, $\Sigma = S^3$ and $S = S^{4n-1}$. Thus

$$\begin{cases} S^{n-1} \text{ is a fibre space (in fact, a covering space)} \\ \quad \text{over } P^{n-1}(R) \text{ with fibre } S^0 \\ S^{2n-1} \text{ is a fibre space over } P^{n-1}(C) \text{ with fibre } S^1 \\ S^{4n-1} \text{ is a fibre space over } P^{n-1}(Q) \text{ with fibre } S^3 \end{cases}$$

Finally, we observe that $P^1(K) = K \cup \{\infty\}$ and therefore $P^1(R) = S^1$, $P^1(C) = S^2$, $P^1(Q) = S^4$. Thus

S^1 is a fibre space over S^1 with fibre S^0
S^3 is a fibre space over S^2 with fibre S^1
S^7 is a fibre space over S^4 with fibre S^3

It is also true that S^{15} is a fibre space over S^8 with fibre S^7; the construction is made by using the nonassociative algebra of Cayley numbers. (For details, see Steenrod, [B.5], p. 109.) The above are the only known fibre maps of spheres onto spheres; they were constructed by Hopf [11].

Before proceeding to the study of homotopy and homology relations in fibre spaces, we need an extension of the covering homotopy theorem.

THEOREM 3.1.6. *Let (W,A) be a finitely triangulable pair such that W and A are contractible, and let $\pi: X \to B$ be a fibre map. Let $f: W \to B$, $g: A \to X$ be maps such that $\pi \circ g = f|A$. Then g has an extension $G: W \to X$ with $\pi \circ G = f$.*

PROOF. If $W = A_0 \times I$, $A = A_0 \times \{0\}$, the conclusion follows from the covering homotopy theorem. It is then easy to prove, by induction on n, that the conclusion holds if $W = A_0 \times I^n$, $A = A_0 \times s_0$.

In the general case, we proceed as follows. Let W_1 be the space obtained from W by collapsing A to a point. Let f_1 be a homeomorphism of W into I^{n-1}, and let λ be a map of W into I such that $\lambda(w) = 0$ if and only if $w \in A$ (e.g.,

$$\lambda(w) = \frac{\rho(w,A)}{1 + \rho(w,A)}$$

where ρ is a metric on W). Define $f_2: W \to I^n = I \times I^{n-1}$ by

$$f_2(w) = (\lambda(w), \lambda(w) \cdot f_1(w))$$

Then $f_2(A) = s_0$ and f_2 induces a homeomorphism of W_1 into I^n.

Now A is contractible, so that $\pi_i(A) = 0$ for all i. Hence the identity map of A into A has extension $r: W \to A$. Define $h: W \to A \times I^n$ by

$$h(w) = (r(w), f_2(w))$$

Then h is a homeomorphism of X into $A \times I^n$ and $h(a) = (a, s_0)$ for all $a \in A$.

Since W is contractible, it follows that $h(W)$ is a retract of $A \times I^n$. Hence the map $f \circ h^{-1}: h(W) \to B$ has an extension $f': A \times I^n \to B$, and $\pi g(a) = f(a) = fh^{-1}(a,s_0) = f'(a,s_0)$ for all $a \in A$. Hence there is a map $G': A \times I^n \to X$ with $\pi \circ G' = f'$, and $G'(a,s_0) = g(a)$. Define $G: W \to X$ by $G = G' \circ h$. Then G is the desired map.

COROLLARY 3.1.7. *Let (W,A) be a relative* CW *complex (W compact) and let $g: W \times 0 \cup A \times I \to X$, $f: W \times I \to B$ be maps such that $\pi \circ g = f | W \times 0 \cup A \times I$. Then g has an extension $G: W \times I \to X$ with $\pi \circ G = f$.*

PROOF. Assume first that W is an n-cell, $A = \dot{W}$. Then

$$(W \times I, W \times 0 \cup A \times I)$$

is homeomorphic with (I^{n+1}, J^n); since I^{n+1} and J^n are contractible, the conclusion follows from Theorem 3.1.6. The extension to the general case is standard.

3.2 The Homotopy Sequence of a Fibre Space [15]

Let $\pi: X \to B$ be a fibre map, $b_0 \in B$, $F = \pi^{-1}(b_0)$, and $x_0 \in F$. We shall use x_0 and b_0 as base points for the appropriate homotopy groups.

THEOREM 3.2.1. $\pi_*: \pi_i(X,F) \approx \pi_i(B,b_0)$ *for* $i \geq 1$.

PROOF. π_* is onto; for let $\alpha \in \pi_n(B,b_0)$ and let $f: (I^n, \dot{I}^n) \to (B,b_0)$ be a map representing α. Define $g: J^{n-1} \to X$ to be the constant map into x_0. Now I^n and J^{n-1} are contractible; by Theorem 3.1.6, g has an extension $G:I^n \to X$ with $\pi_0 \circ G = f$. Then $G:(I^n,\dot{I}^n,J^{n-1}) \to (X,F,x_0)$ represents an element $\alpha' \in \pi_n(X,F)$; clearly $\pi_*(\alpha') = \alpha$. Furthermore, π_* is an isomorphism. For suppose that $\alpha \in \pi_n(X,F)$ and $\pi_*(\alpha) = 0$. Let $g:(I^n,\dot{I}^n,J^{n-1}) \to (X,F,x_0)$ be a representative of α. The map

$$\pi \circ g:(I^n,\dot{I}^n) \to (B,b_0)$$

is homotopic rel $\dot{I}^n$ to the constant map into b_0. By Corollary 3.1.7, g is homotopic rel $\dot{I}^n$ to a map g_1 with $\pi \circ g_1(I^n) = b_0$. Hence $\alpha = 0$.

The proof needs to be modified slightly if $n = 1$. For $\pi_1(X,F)$ is not a group and therefore the fact that Kernel $\pi_* = 0$ does not obviously imply that π_* is 1:1. This is left to the reader.

REMARK 3.2.2. *If $\pi:X \to B$ is a fibre mapping and $A \subset B$, then*

$$\pi|\pi^{-1}(A):\pi^{-1}(A) \to A$$

is a fibre mapping as well. This follows at once from the definition.

COROLLARY 3.2.3. *If A is a nonempty subset of B, $W = \pi^{-1}(A)$ then $\pi_*:\pi_i(X,W) \approx \pi_i(B,A)$ for all $i \geq 1$.*

This follows from the five-lemma, Theorem 2.1, and the previous remark.

COROLLARY 3.2.4. *There is an exact sequence*

$$\cdots \to \pi_n(F_0) \xrightarrow{i_*} \pi_n(X) \xrightarrow{\pi_*} \pi_n(B) \xrightarrow{d_*} \pi_{n-1}(F_0) \to \cdots$$

where d_* is the composition of the homomorphisms

$$\partial_*:\pi_n(X,F_0) \to \pi_{n-1}(F_0)$$

and

$$\pi_*^{-1}:\pi_n(B) \to \pi_n(X,F_0)$$

This sequence is called the homotopy sequence of (X,B,π)

REMARK 3.2.5.

1. $\pi_q(P^n(R)) \approx \begin{cases} Z_2 & q = 1 \\ \pi_q(S^n) & q > 1 \end{cases}$
   if $n > 1$

2. $\pi_q(P^n(C)) \approx \begin{cases} Z & q = 2 \\ \pi_q(S^{2n+1}) & \textit{otherwise} \end{cases}$

3. $\pi_q(P^n(Q)) \approx \pi_q(S^{4n+3}) \oplus \pi_{q-1}(S^3)$

PROOF. Part 1 follows from the fact that S^n is a two-sheeted covering space of $P^n(R)$. Part 2 follows at once from Corollary 3.2.4 and the fact that S^{2n+1} is a fibre space over $P^n(C)$ with fibre S^1. Part 3 is left as an exercise for the reader.

COROLLARY 3.2.6.
$$\left.\begin{aligned} H_q(P^n(R)) &\approx H_q(Z_2,1) \\ H^q(P^n(R)) &\approx H^q(Z_2,1)\end{aligned}\right\} \quad q < n-1$$
$$\left.\begin{aligned} H_q(P^n(C)) &\approx H_q(Z,2) \\ H^q(P^n(C)) &\approx H^q(Z,2)\end{aligned}\right\} \quad q < 2n$$

3.3 The Bundles of Groups $H_q(F;G)$ [19]

Let $\pi : X \to B$ be a fibre map, $b_0 \in B$, $F_0 = \pi^{-1}(b_0)$, $x_0 \in F_0$. We assume that B and F_0 are 0-connected; it follows easily that X is 0-connected. In the subsequent sections, we shall consider only singular cubes with vertices at b_0 and x_0. We shall show how the group $\pi_1(B,b_0)$ operates on $H_q(F_0;G)$. Let ϕ be a loop in B, based at b_0.

THEOREM 3.3.1. *There is a homomorphism* $C_\phi : Q(F_0) \to Q(X)$ *such that*
1. *If f is a singular n-cube in F_0, $C_\phi(f)$ is an $(n+1)$-cube in X.*
2. $C_p(f) \circ \alpha_1^0 = f$.
3. $\pi C_\phi(f)(t,\cdots,t_{n+1}) = \phi(t_1)$.
4. $C_\phi(f \circ \alpha_i^\epsilon) = C_\phi(f) \circ \alpha_{i+1}^\epsilon \qquad (i = 1,\cdots,n)$.
5. *f degenerate $\Rightarrow$ $C_\phi(f)$ degenerate.*

PROOF. We construct C_ϕ over the n-cubes of F_0 by induction on n. There is only one 0-cube in F_0, namely the point x_0. Now ϕ is homotopic rel 0 to the constant map $I \to b_0$. Hence the constant map $I \to x_0$ is homotopic rel 0 to a map $g : I \to X$ such that $\pi \circ g = \phi$. Now F_0 is 0-connected and therefore there is a path $h : I \to F_0$ such that $h(0) = g(1)$ and $h(1) = x_0$. Then $\pi \circ (g \cdot h) = \phi \cdot \theta_{b_0}$. Now $\phi \cdot \theta_{b_0}$ is homotopic rel $\dot{I}$ to ϕ; hence $g \cdot h$ is homotopic rel $\dot{I}$ to a map k such that $\pi \circ k = \phi$. Then k is a 1-cube in X with vertices at x_0. Define $C_\phi(x_0) = k$. Then Parts 1 through 5 clearly hold.

Suppose that C_ϕ has been defined for all cubes of dimension $<n$. Let f be an n-cube in F_0. If f is degenerate, we have $f(t_1,\cdots,t_n) = g(t_1,\cdots,t_{n-1})$ where g is an $(n-1)$-cube. Define $C_\phi(f)$ by

$$C_\phi(f)(t_1,\cdots,t_{n+1}) = C_\phi(g)(t_1,\cdots,t_n)$$

Then Parts 1 and 5 are trivial and Parts 2, 3, and 4 are easily verified, using the inductive hypothesis.

Suppose that f is nondegenerate. Define $g : 0 \times I^n \cup I \times \dot{I}^n \to X$, $h : I^n \to B$ by

$$\begin{cases} g(0,t_2,\cdots,t_{n+1}) = f(t_2,\cdots,t_{n+1}) \\ g(\alpha_{i+1}^{\epsilon}(t_1,\cdots,t_n)) = C_\phi(f \circ \alpha_i^{\epsilon})(t_1,\cdots,t_n) \\ h(t_1,\cdots,t_{n+1}) = \phi(t_1) \end{cases}$$

Then it is easily verified, using the inductive hypothesis, that g is continuous and that $\pi \circ g = h|0 \times I^n \cup I \times \dot{I}^n$. By Theorem 3.1.6 g has an extension $G: I^{n+1} \to X$ such that $\pi \circ G = h$. Define $C_\phi(f) = G$. Then Parts 1 through 5 are trivially verified. This completes the induction.

THEOREM 3.3.2. *Let ϕ_0,ϕ_1 be homotopic loops* (rel $\dot{I}$) *in B, and let C_{ϕ_0}, C_{ϕ_1}, be homomorphisms satisfying Parts* 1 *through* 5 *of Theorem* 3.3.1. *Let $\Phi: I^2 \to B$ be a homotopy of ϕ_0 to ϕ_1* rel $\dot{I}$. *Then there is a homomorphism $D_\Phi: Q(F_0) \to Q(X)$ such that*

1. *If $f: I^n \to F_0$ is an n-cube, then $D_\Phi(f): I^{n+2} \to X$ is an* $(n + 2)$*-cube.*
2. $D_\Phi(f)(0,t_1,\cdots,t_{n+1}) = f(t_2,\cdots,t_{n+1})$.
3. $D_\Phi(f) \circ \alpha_2^{\epsilon} = C_{\phi_\epsilon}(f) \quad (\epsilon = 0,1)$.
4. $\pi D_\Phi(f)(t_1,t_2,\cdots,t_{n+2}) = \Phi(t_1,t_2)$.
5. $D_\Phi(f) \circ \alpha_{i+2}^{\epsilon} = D_\Phi(f \circ \alpha_i^{\epsilon}) \quad (i = 1,\cdots,n)$.
6. *f degenerate $\Rightarrow D_\Phi(f)$ degenerate.*

PROOF. Similar to that of Theorem 3.3.1. Suppose that f is a 0-cube. Define $g: I \times \dot{I} \cup 0 \times I \to X$ by

$$\begin{cases} g(s,\epsilon) = C_{\phi_\epsilon}(f)(s) \\ g(0,t) = x_0 \end{cases}$$

Then $\pi \circ g = \Phi|I \times \dot{I} \cup 0 \times I$, and therefore g has an extension $G: I \times I \to X$. Define $D_\Phi(f) = G$.

Suppose that $D_\Phi(f)$ has been defined for all cubes of dimension $<n$ in F_0. If f is degenerate, so that $f(t_1,\cdots,t_n) = g(t_1,\cdots,t_{n-1})$ for some $(n - 1)$-cube g, define

$$D_\Phi(f)(t_1,\cdots,t_{n+2}) = D_\Phi(g)(t_1,\cdots,t_{n+1})$$

If f is nondegenerate, define $g: J^{n+1} = 0 \times (I \times I^n) \cup I \times (\dot{I} \times I^n) \cup I \times (I \times \dot{I}^n) \to X$, $h: I^{n+2} \to B$ by

$$\begin{cases} g(0,t_1,\cdots,t_{n+1}) = f(t_2,\cdots,t_{n+1}) \\ g(t_1,\epsilon,t_2,\cdots,t_{n+1}) = C_{\phi_\epsilon}(f)(t_1,\cdots,t_{n+1}) \\ g(\alpha_{i+2}^{\epsilon}(t_1,\cdots,t_{n+1})) = D_\Phi(f \circ \alpha_i^{\epsilon})(t_1,\cdots,t_{n+1}) \\ h(t_1,\cdots,t_{n+2}) = \Phi(t_1,t_2) \end{cases}$$

Then $h|I \times \dot{I} \times I^n \cup 0 \times I \times I^n \cup I \times I \times \dot{I}^n = \pi \circ g$, whence g has an extension $G: I^{n+2} \to X$ with $\pi \circ G = h$. Define $D_\Phi(f) = G$. In either case we verify Parts 1 through 6 using the inductive hypothesis. This completes the proof.

Let ϕ be a loop in B and let C_ϕ be a homomorphism as in Theorem 3.3.1. Define $T_\phi: Q(F_0) \to Q(F_0)$ by

$$T_\phi(f) = C_\phi(f) \circ \alpha_1^1$$

Then it is clear that $T_\phi(f)$ induces a chain-mapping $C(F_0) \to C(F_0)$. If ϕ_0,ϕ_1 are homotopic loops and Φ a homotopy rel $\dot{I}$ of ϕ_0 to ϕ_1, define $U_\Phi: Q(F_0) \to Q(F_0)$ by

$$U_\Phi(f) = D_\Phi(f) \circ \alpha_1^1$$

Then U_Φ is a chain homotopy of T_{ϕ_2} to T_{ϕ_1}. Thus to each loop ϕ in B we may associate the induced homomorphism $T_\phi: H(F_0;G) \to H(F_0;G)$; if ϕ_0,ϕ_1 are homotopic loops then $T_{\phi_0} = T_{\phi_1}: H(F_0;G) \to H(F_0;G)$. Thus for any $\xi \in \pi_1(B,b_0)$ we may define $T_\xi: H(F_0;G) \to H(F_0;G)$; $T_\xi = T_\phi$ for any $\phi \in \xi$.

THEOREM 3.3.3. *$\pi_1(B,b_0)$ operates on $H(F_0;G)$ via the operation T_ξ.*

PROOF. We need to verify: $T_\epsilon =$ identity, $T_{\xi\eta} = T_\xi \circ T_\eta$. The first is trivial, for we may choose $\phi = e_{b_0}$, $C_\phi(f)(t_1,\cdots,t_{n+1}) = f(t_2,\cdots,t_{n+1})$. Then $T_\phi(f) = f$, and $\therefore$ $T_\epsilon =$ identity. To prove the second, let $\phi \in \xi$, $\psi \in \eta$ and let C_ϕ, C_ψ be homomorphisms as in Theorem 3.3.1. Define $C_{\phi\psi}: Q(F_0) \to Q(X)$ by

$$C_{\phi\psi}(f)(t_1,\cdots,t_{n+1}) = \begin{cases} C_\phi(f)(2t_1,t_2,\cdots,t_{n+1}) & 0 \leq t_1 \leq \frac{1}{2} \\ C_\psi(T_\phi(f))(2t_1 - 1,t_2,\cdots,t_{n+1}) & \frac{1}{2} \leq t_1 \leq 1 \end{cases}$$

Then $C_{\phi\psi}$ satisfies the conditions of Theorem 3.3.1 and $T_{\phi\psi} = T_\psi \circ T_\phi$. Hence

$$T_{\xi\eta} = T_{\phi\psi} = T_{\psi\phi} = T_\phi \circ T_\psi = T_\xi \circ T_\eta$$

REMARK. *We may use a similar argument to show*

1. *$\pi_1(B)$ operates on the groups $H^q(F_0;G)$.*
2. *If B is 0-connected, then for any $b_0,b_1 \in B$, the spaces $\pi^{-1}(b_0)$ and $\pi^{-1}(b_1)$ have chain-equivalent total cubical complexes (and therefore isomorphic homology and cohomology groups).*
3. *Under the same hypothesis, $\pi^{-1}(b_0)$ and $\pi^{-1}(b_1)$ have isomorphic homotopy groups.*
4. *If F_0 is n-simple, then $\pi_1(B)$ operates on $\pi_n(F_0)$. In view of Part 2, we will henceforth refer to F_0 simply as F.*

3.4 Filtration of the Chain-Groups of X; the Spectral Sequence [17, 19]

We now introduce a machinery for investigating homology relations between X, B, and F. This machinery was invented by Leray [17] for the case of the Čech groups. For the applications to homotopy theory it is preferable to use singular groups; the adaptation of Leray's theory to singular groups was made by Serre [19]; we shall refer to this paper as S. The idea is to measure, in some sense, the extent to which X fails to be a product space of B with F. If $X = B \times F$, it follows from the Künneth theorems that, for any coefficient group G, $H(X;G) \approx H(B;H(F;G))$; the "deviation" in the general case is measured by a sequence of abstract complexes $E_2, E_3, \cdots$ such that $E_2 = H(B;H(F;G))$ (provided $\pi_1(B)$ acts trivially on $H(F;G)$) and $E_{i+1} = H(E_i)$. Furthermore, $H(X)$ has a sequence $J^0 \subset J^1 \subset \cdots \subset J^n \subset \cdots$ of subgroups, and the group $\sum_{i=0} \oplus J^i/J^{i-1}$ is, in a certain sense, the direct limit of the groups E_i.

Let $T^{p,q}$ be the subgroup of $Q_{p+q}(X)$ spanned by all cubes u whose projections into B are q times degenerate in the sense that

$$\pi u(t_1,\cdots,t_{p+q}) = \pi u(t_1,\cdots,t_p,0,\cdots,0)$$

for all $t = (t_1,\cdots,t_{p+q}) \in I^{p+q}$. Let $A^{p,q} = T^{p,q}/(T^{p,q} \cap D_{p+q}(X))$. We note the following relations:

$$(1)\qquad \begin{cases} T^{p,q} \subset T^{p+1,q-1} \\ T^{p,0} = Q_p(X) \\ T^{0,p} = Q_p(F) \\ T^{-1,p} = 0 \end{cases}$$

and therefore

$$(2)\qquad \begin{cases} A^{p,q} \subset A^{p+1,q-1} \\ A^{p,0} = C_p(X) \\ A^{0,p} = C_p(F) \\ A^{-1,p} = 0 \end{cases}$$

LEMMA 3.4.1. *Let $u \in T^{p,q}$. Then*

1. $u \circ \alpha_i^\epsilon \in T^{p-1,q}$ *if $i \leq p$.*
2. $u \circ \alpha_i^\epsilon \in T^{p,q-1}$ *if $i > p$.*
3. $\partial u \in T^{p,q-1}$.

PROOF. We have

$$\begin{aligned} \pi \circ u \circ \alpha_i^\epsilon(t_i,\cdots,t_{p+q-1}) &= \pi \circ u(t_1,\cdots,t_{i-1},\epsilon,t_i,\cdots,t_{p+q-1}) \\ &= \begin{cases} \pi \circ u(t_1,\cdots,t_{i-1},\epsilon,t_i,\cdots,t_{p-1},0,\cdots,0) & (i \leq p) \\ \pi \circ u(t_i,\cdots,t_p,0,\cdots,0) & (i > p) \end{cases} \\ &= \begin{cases} \pi \circ u \circ \alpha_i^\epsilon(t_i,\cdots,t_{p-1},0,\cdots,0) & (i \leq p) \\ \pi \circ u \circ \alpha_i^\epsilon(t_1,\cdots,t_p,0,\cdots,0) & (i > p) \end{cases} \end{aligned}$$

and Parts 1 and 2 follow. Of course, Part 3 follows from Parts 1 and 2.

Let G be an abelian group. Now it is clear from the definitions that $A^{p,q}$ is a direct factor of $C_{p+q}(X)$ and therefore $A^{p,q} \otimes G$ is a subgroup of $C_{p+q}(X;G)$. We define $A^{p,q}(G) = A^{p,q} \otimes G$, $A^p(G) = \sum_q A^{p,q}(G)$. The following statements are immediate:

$$\begin{cases} 1.\ A^p(G) \text{ is a subgroup of } C(X;G). \\ 2.\ A^p(G) \cap C_{p+q}(X;G) = A^{p,q}(G). \\ 3.\ A^p(G) \subset A^{p+1}(G). \\ 4.\ A^{p,q}(G) = C_{p+q}(X;G) \text{ if } q \leq 0. \\ 5.\ A^{p,q}(G) = 0 \text{ if } p < 0. \\ 6.\ A^{0,p}(G) = C_p(F;G). \\ 7.\ \partial A^p(G) \subset A^p(G). \end{cases}$$

The sequence of subgroups $\{A^p(G)\}$ is called a *filtration* of $C(X;G)$. It gives rise to a filtration of $H(X;G)$. Define $J^{p,q}(G) =$ the image of $A^{p,q}(G)$ in

$$H_{p+q}(X;G) = \frac{A^{p,q}(G) \cap Z_{p+q}(X;G)}{A^{p,q}(G) \cap B_{p+q}(X;G)}$$

Also let $J^p(G) = \sum_q \oplus J^{p,q}(G) \subset H(X;G)$. The groups $J^{p,q}(G)$ satisfy conditions analogous to Parts 1 through 6. Thus

$$0 = J^{-1,n+1}(G) \subset J^{0,n}(G) \subset \cdots \subset J^{n,0}(G) = H_n(X;G)$$

We may also consider the successive factor groups

$$E_\infty^{p,q}(G) = \frac{J^{p,q}(G)}{J^{p-1,q+1}(G)}$$

$$E_\infty^p(G) = \frac{J^p(G)}{J^{p-1}(G)} = \sum_q \oplus E_\infty^{p,q}(G)$$

Finally we may define

$$E_\infty(G) = \sum_p \oplus E_\infty^p(G)$$

The group $E_\infty(G)$ is not in general isomorphic with $H(X;G)$; however, in certain important cases it is (e.g., if G is a field).

In a similar manner we may consider the sequence

$$0 = A^{-1,n+1}(G) \subset A^{0,n}(G) \subset \cdots \subset A^{n,0}(G) = C_n(X;G)$$

and the successive factor groups

$$E_0^{p,q}(G) = \frac{A^{p,q}(G)}{A^{p-1,q+1}(G)}$$

$$E_0^p(G) = \frac{A^p(G)}{A^{p-1}(G)} = \sum_q \oplus E_0^{p,q}(G)$$

$$E_0(G) = \sum_p \oplus E_0^p(G)$$

The spectral sequence gives us a machinery for making the transition from $E_0(G)$ to $E_\infty(G)$. As a beginning we may observe that since $\partial A^p(G) \subset A^p(G)$, $\partial A^{p-1}(G) \subset A^{p-1}(G)$, there is an induced homomorphism $d_0: E_0^p(G) \to E_0^p(G)$ of square zero. Thus E_0 is an abstract complex with d_0 as boundary operator. We now proceed to the definition of the intermediate complexes $E_1, E_2, \cdots$. For simplicity, in the remainder of this section, we abbreviate $A^{p,q}(G)$ to $A^{p,q}$, etc.

Before giving the definition of E_r we give a list of formulas from group theory which will be useful in the subsequent calculations.

Let G be an abelian group. In what follows we ignore the distinction between two groups which are isomorphic by one of the Noether isomorphism theorems. Let A, B, C be subgroups of G. Then

1. $\dfrac{A+B}{B} = \dfrac{A}{A \cap B}$ (first isomorphism theorem).

2. If $A \supset B \supset C$, then
   $\dfrac{A/C}{B/C} = \dfrac{A}{B}$ (second isomorphism theorem).

3. If $A \supset B$, then
   $(B + C) \cap A = B + (C \cap A)$ (modular law)
   and we may therefore abbreviate both to
$$B + C \cap A = A \cap C + B$$

4. If $B \supset C$, then
$$\frac{A+B}{A+C} = \frac{B}{B \cap A + C}$$

5. If $B \supset C$, then
$$\frac{A \cap B}{A \cap C} = \frac{C + A \cap B}{C}$$

Let G, G' be abelian groups, $f: G \to G'$ a homomorphism. Then (unprimed letters denote subgroups of G, primed letters subgroup of G'):

$$\begin{aligned} f(A + B) &= f(A) + f(B) \\ f(A \cap f^{-1}(B')) &= f(A) \cap B' \\ f^{-1}(A' \cap B') &= f^{-1}(A') \cap f^{-1}(B') \\ f^{-1}(A' + f(B)) &= f^{-1}(A') + B \end{aligned}$$

Suppose further that $A \supset B$, $A' \supset B'$, and that $f(A) \subset A'$, $f(B) \subset B'$. Then f induces $\bar{f}: A/B \to A'/B'$, and

$$\text{Kernel}\, \bar{f} = \frac{A \cap f^{-1}(B')}{B}$$

$$\text{Image}\, \bar{f} = \frac{f(A) + B'}{B'}$$

Now define

$$C_r^p = A^p \cap \partial^{-1}A^{p-r}, \; C_r^{p,q} = C_r^p \cap A^{p,q}$$
$$D_r^p = A^p \cap \partial A^{p+r}, \; D_r^{p,q} = D_r^p \cap A^{p,q}$$
$$E_r^p = \frac{C_r^p}{C_{r-1}^{p-1} + D_{r-1}^p}, \; E_r^{p,q} = \frac{C_r^{p,q}}{C_{r-1}^{p-1,q+1} + D_{r-1}^{p,q}}$$
$$E_r = \sum_p \oplus E_r^p = \sum_{p,q} \oplus E_r^{p,q}$$

To see that E_r^p is well defined, note that

$$C_{r-1}^{p-1} = A^{p-1} \cap \partial^{-1}A^{p-r} \subset A^p \cap \partial^{-1}A^{p-r} = C_r^p$$
$$D_{r-1}^p = A^p \cap \partial A^{p+r+1} \subset A^p \cap \partial^{-1}A^{p-r} = C_r^p$$

To see that our definition of E_0 agrees with the old one, note that

$$C_0^p = A^p \cap \partial^{-1}A^p = A^p \text{ since } \partial A^p \subset A^p$$
$$C_{-1}^{p-1} = A^{p-1} \cap \partial^{-1}A^p = A^{p-1} \text{ since } A^{p-1} \subset A^p \subset \partial^{-1}A^p$$
$$D_{-1}^p = A^p \cap \partial \cdot A^{p-1} = \partial A^{p-1} \subset A^{p-1}$$

so that

$$\frac{C_0^p}{C_{-1}^{p-1} + D_{-1}^p} = \frac{A^p}{A^{p-1} + \partial A^{p-1}} = \frac{A^p}{A^{p-1}}$$

LEMMA 3.4.2. *∂ induces an endomorphism $d_r: E_r \to E_r$. We also have $d_r(E_r^{p,q}) \subset E_r^{p-r,q+r-1}$ and $d_r \circ d_r = 0$.*

PROOF. We have to show:

1. $\partial C_r^p \subset C_r^{p-r}$.
2. $\partial(C_{r-1}^{p-1} + D_{r-1}^p) \subset C_{r-1}^{p-r-1} + D_{r-1}^{p-r}$.

Now

$$\begin{aligned}\partial C_r^p &= \partial(A^p \cap \partial^{-1}(A^{p-r})) \\ &= \partial A^p \cap A^{p-r} \subset A^{p-r} \cap \partial^{-1}A^{p-2r} = C_r^{p-r}\end{aligned}$$
$$\begin{aligned}\partial C_{r-1}^{p-1} &= \partial(A^{p-1} \cap \partial^{-1}A^{p-r}) = A^{p-r} \cap \partial A^{p-1} \\ &= D_{r-1}^{p-r}\end{aligned}$$
$$\partial D_{r-1}^p = 0$$

and Parts 1 and 2 follow. The rest is trivial.

THEOREM 3.4.3. $E_{r+1} = H(E_r)$.

PROOF. We first claim

1. (Kernel d_r) $\cap E_r^p = \dfrac{C_{r+1}^p + C_{r-1}^{p-1}}{C_{r-1}^{p-1} + D_{r-1}^p}$.
2. (Image d_r) $\cap E_r^p = \dfrac{C_{r-1}^{p-1} + D_r^p}{C_{r-1}^{p-1} + D_{r-1}^p}$.

Proof of Part 1

$$(\text{Kernel } d_r) \cap E_r^p = \frac{C_r^p \cap \partial^{-1}[C_{r-1}^{p-r-1} + D_{r-1}^{p-r}]}{C_{r-1}^{p-1} + D_{r-1}^{p}}$$

But $D_{r-1}^{p-r} = A^{p-r} \cap \partial A^{p-1} = \partial(A^{p-1} \cap \partial^{-1}A^{p-r}) = \partial C_{r-1}^{p-1}$; hence

$$\begin{aligned} C_r^p \cap \partial^{-1}[C_{r-1}^{p-r-1} + D_{r-1}^{p-r}] &= C_r^p \cap \partial^{-1}[C_{r-1}^{p-r-1} + \partial C_{r-1}^{p-1}] \\ &= C_r^p \cap [C_{r-1}^{p-1} + \partial^{-1}C_{r-1}^{p-r-1}] \\ &= C_{r-1}^{p-1} + [C_r^p \cap \partial^{-1}C_{r-1}^{p-r-1}] \\ &\qquad\qquad (\text{since } C_r^p \supset C_{r-1}^{p-1}) \\ &= C_{r-1}^{p-1} + [A^p \cap \partial^{-1}A^{p-r} \\ &\qquad \cap \partial^{-1}(A^{p-r-1} \cap \partial^{-1}A^{p-2r})] \\ &= C_{r-1}^{p-1} + [A^p \cap \partial^{-1}A^{p-r-1}] \\ &= C_{r-1}^{p-1} + C_{r+1}^p \end{aligned}$$

Proof of Part 2

$$(\text{Image } d_r) \cap E_r^p = \partial C_r^{p+r} + \frac{[C_{r-1}^{p-1} + D_{r-1}^p]}{C_{r-1}^{p-1} + D_{r-1}^p}$$

and

$$\begin{aligned} \partial C_r^{p+r} + C_{r-1}^{p-1} + D_{r-1}^p &= D_r^p + C_{r-1}^{p-1} + D_{r-1}^p \\ &= C_{r-1}^{p-1} + D_r^p \text{ since } D_r^p \supset D_{r-1}^p \end{aligned}$$

Now

$$\begin{aligned} H(E_r) = \frac{\text{Kernel } d_r}{\text{Image } d_r} &= \sum_p \oplus \frac{(\text{Kernel } d_r) \cap E_r^p}{(\text{Image } d_r) \cap E_r^p} \\ &= \sum_p \oplus \frac{C_{r+1}^p + C_{r-1}^{p-1}}{D_r^p + C_{r-1}^{p-1}} \\ &= \sum_p \oplus \frac{C_{r+1}^p}{C_{r+1}^p \cap [C_{r-1}^{p-1} + D_r^p]} \\ &= \sum_p \oplus \frac{C_{r+1}^p}{D_r^p + [C_{r+1}^p \cap C_{r-1}^{p-1}]} \text{ since } C_{r+1}^p \supset D_r^p \end{aligned}$$

But

$$\begin{aligned} C_{r+1}^p \cap C_{r-1}^{p-1} &= A^p \cap \partial^{-1}A^{p-r-1} \cap A^{p-1} \cap \partial^{-1}A^{p-r} \\ &= A^{p-1} \cap \partial^{-1}A^{p-r-1} = C_r^{p-1} \end{aligned}$$

Thus finally

$$\begin{aligned} H(E_r) &= \sum_p \oplus \frac{C_{r+1}^p}{C_r^{p-1} + D_r^p} \\ &= \sum_p \oplus E_{r+1}^p = E_{r+1} \end{aligned}$$

THEOREM 3.4.4. *If* $r > \max(p, q+1)$, *then* $E_r^{p,q} = E_\infty^{p,q}$.

PROOF. We have

$$J^{p,q} = \frac{[A^{p,q} \cap Z_{p+q}(X)] + B_{p+q}(X)}{B_{p+q}(X)}$$

so that

$$\begin{aligned} E_\infty^{p,q} &= \frac{J^{p,q}}{J^{p-1,q-1}} \\ &= \frac{[A^{p,q} \cap Z_{p+q}(X)] + B_{p+q}(X)}{[A^{p-1,q+1} \cap Z_{p+q}(X)] + B_{p+q}(X)} \\ &= \frac{A^{p,q} \cap Z_{p+q}(X)}{[A^{p-1,q+1} \cap Z_{p+q}(X)] + [A^{p,q} \cap B_{p+q}(X)]} \end{aligned}$$

Now if $r > p$, $r > q + 1$, then $A^{p-r,q+r-1} = 0$ and $A^{p+r-1,q-r+2} = C_{p+q+1}(X)$, so that

$$\begin{aligned} C_r^{p,q} &= A^{p,q} \cap \partial^{-1}A^{p-r,q+r-1} = A^{p,q} \cap Z_{p+q}(X) \\ C_{r-1}^{p-1,q+1} &= A^{p-1,q+1} \cap \partial^{-1}A^{p-r,q+r-1} = A^{p-1,q+1} \cap Z_{p+q}(X) \\ D_{r-1}^{p,q} &= A^{p,q} \cap \partial A^{p+r-1,q-r+2} = A^{p,q} \cap B_{p+q}(X) \end{aligned}$$

and it follows that

$$E_r^{p,q} = E_\infty^{p,q}$$

as desired.

3.5 Calculation of $E_1(G)$ and $E_2(G)$ [19]

In this section we omit many of the rather lengthy proofs, referring the reader to reference 19.

Let $u \in T^{p,q}$. We define cubes $B^p u \in Q_p(B)$, $F^p u \in Q_q(F)$ by

$$\begin{cases} B^p u(t_1, \cdots, t_p) = \pi \circ u(t_1, \cdots, t_p, 0, \cdots, 0) \\ F^p u(t_1, \cdots, t_q) = u(0, \cdots, 0, t_1, \cdots, t_q) \end{cases}$$

If u is degenerate, then $F^p u$ is degenerate; if $u \in T^{p-1,q+1}$, then $B^p u$ is degenerate. Now

$$\begin{aligned} A^{p,q} &= T^{p,q} + D_{p+q}(X) \\ A^{p-1,q+1} &= T^{p-1,q+1} + D_{p+q}(X) \end{aligned}$$

and therefore

$$E_0^{p,q} = \frac{T^{p,q} + D_{p+q}(X)}{T^{p-1,q+1} + D_{p+q}(X)} = \frac{T^{p,q}}{T^{p-1,q+1} + [T^{p,q} \cap D_{p+q}(X)]}$$

Define a homomorphism $\tilde{K}: T^{p,q} \to Q_p(B) \otimes Q_q(F)$ by

$$\tilde{K}u = (B^p u) \otimes (F^p u)$$

It follows that $\tilde{K}$ induces a homomorphism $K: E_0 \to C(B) \otimes C(F)$ with $K(E_0^{p,q}) \subset C_p(B) \otimes C_q(F)$.

LEMMA 3.5.1. *Define d on* $C(B) \otimes C(F)$ *by*

$$d(a \otimes b) = (-1)^p a \otimes \partial b \qquad a \in C_p(B),\ b \in C(F)$$

Then $K: E_0 \to C(B) \otimes C(F)$ *is a chain-mapping.*

PROOF. Let $u \in T^{p,q}$. Then

$$\begin{aligned} \overline{K}(\partial a) &= \overline{K}\left(\sum_{i,\epsilon} (-1)^{i+\epsilon} u \circ \alpha_i^\epsilon\right) \\ &= \sum_{i,\epsilon} (-1)^{i+\epsilon} B^p(u \circ \alpha_i^\epsilon) \otimes F^p(u \circ \alpha_i^\epsilon) \end{aligned}$$

If $i \leq p$, it follows from Lemma 3.4.1 that $u \circ \alpha_i^\epsilon \in T^{p-1,q}$ and therefore $B^p(u \circ \alpha_i^\epsilon)$ is degenerate. If $i > p$, then

$$\begin{aligned} B^p(u \circ \alpha_i^\epsilon)(t_1,\cdots,t_p) &= \pi \circ u(\alpha_i^\epsilon(t_1,\cdots,t_p,0,\cdots,0)) \\ &= \pi \circ u(t_1,\cdots,t_p,0,\cdots,\epsilon,\cdots,0) \\ &= \pi \circ u(t_1,\cdots,t_p,0,\cdots,0) \\ &= B_u^p(t_1,\cdots,t_p) \end{aligned}$$

while

$$\begin{aligned} F^p(u \circ \alpha_i^\epsilon)(t_1,\cdots,t_q) &= u(\alpha_i^\epsilon(0,\cdots,0,t_i,\cdots,t_{q-1})) \\ &= u(0,\cdots,0,t_1,\cdots,t_{i-p-1},\epsilon,t_{i-p},\cdots,t_{q-1}) \\ &= F_u^p(\alpha_{i-p}^\epsilon(t_1,\cdots,t_{q-1})) \end{aligned}$$

Thus if $\bar{u}$ is the element of $E_0^{p,q}$ represented by u, we have

$$\begin{aligned} Kd_0\bar{u} &= \sum_{i=p+1}^{p+q} \sum_{\epsilon=0}^{1} (-1)^{i+\epsilon}(B^p u) \otimes [(F^p u) \circ \alpha_{i-p}^\epsilon] \\ &= (-1)^p B^p u \otimes \sum_{j=1}^{q} \sum_{\epsilon=0}^{1} (-1)^{j+\epsilon}(F^p u) \circ \alpha_j^\epsilon \\ &= dK\bar{u} \end{aligned}$$

THEOREM 3.5.2. *The chain map* $K: E_0 \to C(B) \otimes C(F)$ *is a chain equivalence.*

PROOF. Part I. We claim that there is a homomorphism $K: Q^p(B) \otimes Q^q(F) \to T^{p,q}$ such that

1. If u is a p-cube in B, v a q cube in F, then $K(u \otimes v)$ is a $(p+q)$-cube in $T^{p,q}$
2. $B^p K(u \otimes v) = u$, $F^p K(u \otimes v) = v$

3. $K(u \otimes [v \circ \alpha_i^\epsilon]) = K(u \otimes v) \circ \alpha_{i+p}^\epsilon (i \leq q, \epsilon = 0,1)$
4. If v is degenerate, $K(u \otimes v)$ is degenerate.

The proof, by induction on q, is given in reference 19, p. 459.

If u is degenerate, then $B^pK(u \otimes v)$ is degenerate by Part 2, and therefore $K(u \otimes v) \in T^{p-1,q+1}$. If v is degenerate, then $K(u \otimes v) \in T^{p,q} \cap D_{p+q}(X)$ by Part 4. Hence K induces a homomorphism $\lambda: C(B) \otimes C(F) \to E_0$ with $\lambda[C_p(B) \otimes C_q(F)] \subset E_0^{p,q}$. It follows from 3 that λ is a chain map, and from 2 that $K \circ \lambda =$ identity.

Part II. We next assert that there is a homomorphism $S^p: T^{p,q} \to T^{p,q+1}$ such that

1. If u is a $(p + q)$-cube, then S^pu is a $(p + q + 1)$-cube.
2. $B^pS^pu = B^pu$.
3. $S^pu(0,\cdots,0,t,t_1,\cdots,t_q) = u(0,\cdots,0,t_1,\cdots,t_q)$.
4. $(S^pu) \circ \alpha_{p+1}^0 = u, (S^pu) \circ \alpha_{p+1}^1 = K(B^pu \otimes F^pu)$.
5. $S^p(u \circ \alpha_i^\epsilon) = (S^pu) \circ \alpha_{i+1}^\epsilon \qquad (i > p, \epsilon = 0,1)$.
6. If $q > 0$ and u is degenerate, then S^pu is degenerate.

For the proof, see reference 19, p. 462.

If $u \in T^{p-1,q+1}$, then B^pu is degenerate; hence B^pS^pu is degenerate and $\therefore$ $S^pu \in T^{p-1,q+2}$. If u is degenerate and $q > 0$, then S^pu is degenerate; if u is degenerate and $q = 0$, then $u \in T^{p-1,q+1}$ and $\therefore$ $S^pu \in T^{p-1,q+2}$. Thus the map $c \to (-1)^pS^pc\ (c \in T^{p,q})$ induces a homomorphism $\Theta: E_0 \to E_0$ such that $\Theta(E_0^{p,q}) \subset E_0^{p,q+1}$. It follows from the remaining properties that Θ is a chain homotopy between $\lambda \circ K$ and the identity.

COROLLARY 3.5.3. *For any coefficient group G,*

$$E_1^{p,q}(G) \approx C_p(B) \otimes H_q(F;G)$$

PROOF. We have $A^p(G) = A^p \otimes G$, whence

$$E_0^p(G) = A^p(G)/A^{p-1}(G) = \frac{A^p \otimes G}{A^{p-1} \otimes G} = (A^p/A^{p-1}) \otimes G = E_0^p \otimes G$$

Thus $E_0(G)$ is chain-equivalent to $C(B) \otimes C(F) \otimes G$. Now $C(B)$ is free and therefore $H(C(B) \otimes C(F) \otimes G) \approx C(B) \otimes H(C(F) \otimes G) = C(B) \otimes H(F;G)$.

We now make a further assumption.

ASSUMPTION. *$\pi_1(B)$ operates trivially on $H(F;G)$. If we do not make this assumption, Corollary 3.5.5 still holds if we use homology with local coefficients instead of ordinary homology in B [19].*

THEOREM 3.5.4. *Define d' on $C(B) \otimes H(F,G)$ by*

$$d'(a \otimes \alpha) = (\partial a) \otimes \alpha$$

Then the homomorphism $K_*: E_1(G) \to C(B) \otimes H(F;G)$ induced by the chain map K is a chain-mapping.

For the proof, see reference 19.

COROLLARY 3.5.5. $E_2^{p,q} \approx H_p(B;H_q(F;G))$.

3.6 Relative Homology in a Fibre Space [18, 20]

Let now B_0 be a subspace of B, $X_0 = \pi^{-1}(B_0)$; then $\pi|X_0: X_0 \to B_0$ is a fibre map. The filtration defined above on $C(X)$ induces a filtration on $C(X_0)$ and also on $C(X)/C(X_0)$; the groups defining these filtrations are

$$*A^p = A^p \cap C(X_0) \subset C(X_0)$$

$$\bar{A}^p = \frac{A^p}{A^p \cap C(X_0)} \subset C(X)/C(X_0)$$

Thus we have three spectral sequences

$$E_r,\ *E_r,\ \bar{E}_r \qquad (r = 0,1,2,\cdots,\infty)$$

and it is trivial that the spectral sequence $*E_r$ is exactly the spectral sequence associated with the fibre map $\pi|X_0: X_0 \to B_0$. Note that $*E_0$ is a subcomplex of E_0 and that $\bar{E}_0 = E_0/*E_0$. Now the chain map $K: E_0 \to C(B) \otimes C(F)$ sends $*E_0$ into $C(B_0) \otimes C(F)$ and therefore induces

$$\bar{K}: \bar{E}_0 \to C(B) \otimes C(F)/C(B_0) \otimes C(F) = (C(B)/C(B_0)) \otimes C(F)$$

Thus we have a commutative diagram

$$\begin{array}{ccccccccc} 0 \longrightarrow & *E_0^p & \longrightarrow & E_0^p & \longrightarrow & \bar{E}_0^p & \longrightarrow 0 \\ & \downarrow{\scriptstyle *K} & & \downarrow{\scriptstyle K} & & \downarrow{\scriptstyle \bar{K}} & \\ 0 \longrightarrow & C(B_0) \otimes C(F) & \longrightarrow & C(B) \otimes C(F) & \longrightarrow & (C(B)/C(B_0)) \otimes C(F) & \longrightarrow 0 \end{array}$$

Now K is a chain equivalence, and $*K$ is the same as the K defined for $\pi|X_0$; thus $*K$ is also a chain equivalence. It follows from the five-lemma that $\bar{K}$ induces isomorphisms of the homology groups. Thus

$$\bar{E}_1^p \approx C_p(B,B_0;H(F))$$

and, in the same way as before, we see that

$$\bar{E}_1^p(G) \approx C_p(B,B_0;H(F;G))$$

Now consider

$$\begin{array}{ccccccc} 0 \to & {}^*E_1^p(G) & \to & E_1^p(G) & \to & \bar{E}_1^p(G) & \to 0 \\ & \downarrow {}^*K_1 & & \downarrow K_1 & & \downarrow \bar{K}_1 & \\ 0 \to & C(B_0) \otimes H(F;G) & \to & C(B) \otimes H(F;G) & \to & (C(B)/C(B_0)) \otimes H(F;G) & \to 0 \end{array}$$

The bottom sequence is exact and the homomorphisms ${}^*K_1$, K_1, $\bar{K}_1$ are isomorphisms onto; hence the top sequence is exact.

3.7 Some Applications of Spectral Sequences [9, 19, 24]

Let us consider the pre-image under d_r of $E_r^{p,0}$ for $r > 1$. This is given by $E_r^{p+r,1-r}$. Since $1 - r < 0$, $E_r^{p+r,1-r} = 0$, and hence $E_r^{p,0}$ contains no boundaries. Hence its pth homology group, $E_{r+1}^{p,0}$, is isomorphic to the subgroup of cycles of $E_r^{p,0}$, and hence we may consider $E_{r+1}^{p,0}$ to be a subgroup of $E_r^{p,0}$. Hence we may set up the sequence

$$H_p(B;G) \approx H_p(B;H_0(F;G)) = E_2^{p,0} \supset E_3^{p,0} \supset \cdots \supset E_p^{p,0} \supset E_{p+1}^{p,0}$$
$$= E_\infty^{p,0} = \frac{J^{p,0}}{J^{p-1,1}}$$

by Corollary 3.5.5, Theorem 3.4.4, and the definition of $E_\infty^{p,q}$. Now $J^{p,0}$ = the image of $A^{p,0}(G)$ in $H_p(X;G)$ = the image of $C_p(X;G)$ in $H_p(X;G) = H_p(X;G)$. Hence there exists a map from $H_p(X;G)$ onto $E_\infty^{p,0}$. If we compose this with the sequence of inclusions in the above sequence, we obtain a map π_* from $H_p(X;G)$ into $H_p(B;G)$; and since π_* is a composition of maps which are induced by inclusions, except for the map from $E_2^{p,0}$ to $H_p(B;G)$, which is induced by the projection π, we have succeeded in proving the following Theorem.

THEOREM 3.7.1. *The map $\pi_*: H_p(X;G) \to H_p(B;G)$ induced by the projection π is the composition of the maps*

$$H_p(X;G) = J^{p,0} \twoheadrightarrow \frac{J^{p,0}}{J^{p-1,1}} = E_\infty^{p,0}$$
$$\approx E_{p+1}^{p,0} \subset E_p^{p,0} \subset \cdots \subset E_3^{p,0} \subset E_2^{p,0} \approx H_p(B;G)$$

all the maps being induced by inclusion, except for the last, which is the isomorphism of 3.5.5.

Similarly, we have that for $r > 0$, $d_r(E_r^{0,q}) = E_r^{-r,q+r-1} = 0$. Hence $E_r^{0,q}$ consists entirely of cycles, and it follows that $E_{r+1}^{0,q} = H_q(E_r^{0,q})$ is a factor group of $E_r^{0,q}$. Hence we have the sequence

$$\begin{aligned} H_q(F;G) &\approx H_0(B;H_q(F;G)) \\ &\approx E_r^{0,q} \twoheadrightarrow E_3^{0,q} \twoheadrightarrow \cdots \twoheadrightarrow E_{q+1}^{0,q} \twoheadrightarrow E_{q+2}^{0,q} \\ &= E_\infty^{0,q} = J^{0,q} \subset H_q(X;G) \end{aligned}$$

We have proved the following Theorem.

THEOREM 3.7.2. *The injection $i_*: H_q(F;G) \to H_q(X;G)$ is a composition of the mappings in the foregoing sequence.*

THEOREM 3.7.3. *If any two of $H_p(B)$, $H_p(F)$, and $H_p(X)$ are finitely generated for all p, so is the third.*

PROOF. 1. Suppose $H_p(B)$ and $H_q(F)$ are finitely generated for all p. We have $E_2^{p,q} \approx H_p(B;H_q(F)) \approx H_p(B) \otimes H_q(F) \oplus H_{p-1}(B) * H_q(F)$, and hence $E_2^{p,q}$ is finitely generated. Let us assume we have proved $E_r^{p,q}$ is finitely generated. Then since $E_{r+1}^{p,q}$ is a factor group of a subgroup of $E_r^{p,q}$, and since $E_r^{p,q}$ is abelian, it follows that $E_{r+1}^{p,q}$ is finitely generated as well. Hence by induction $E_r^{p,q}$ is finitely generated for $r > 1$. Hence $E_\infty^{p,q}$ ($= E_r^{p,q}$ for sufficiently large r) is finitely generated. Now $H_n(X) = J^{n,0} \supset J^{n-1,1} \supset \cdots \supset J^{0,n} \supset J^{-1,n+1} = 0$; and $J^{p,q}/J^{p-1,q+1}$ is finitely generated for every p and q. It follows that $H_n(X)$ is finitely generated.

2. Suppose that $H_p(X)$ and $H_p(B)$ are finitely generated for all p. Suppose that $H_p(F)$ is finitely generated for $p < n$, but $H_n(F)$ is not finitely generated. It follows that $E_2^{0,n} \approx H_n(F)$ is not finitely generated either. Now let us suppose we have shown that $E_r^{0,n}$ is not finitely generated. Then we have

$$E_{r+1}^{0,n} \approx \frac{E_r^{0,n}}{d_r(E_r^{2,n-1})}$$

But from the reasoning of Part 1 it follows that $E_r^{2,n-1}$ is finitely generated, and hence its image under d_r is. Since $E_r^{0,n}$ is by assumption not finitely generated, it follows that $E_{r+1}^{0,n}$ is not finitely generated either. Hence for no $r > 1$ is $E_r^{0,n}$ finitely generated. Hence $E_\infty^{0,n}$ is not finitely generated either. But by Theorem 3.7.2, $E_\infty^{0,n} \subset H_n(X)$ which is finitely generated, and we have arrived at a contradiction.

3. Suppose that $H_p(X)$ and $H_p(F)$ are finitely generated for all p. Suppose that we have shown $H_q(B)$ finitely generated for $q < p$. By Theorem 3.7.1, it follows that $E_{p+1}^{p,0}$ is finitely generated also. Suppose we have shown $E_r^{p,0}$ is finitely generated, $r > 2$. Now $E_r^{p,0}$ consists precisely of the cycles of $E_{r-1}^{p,0}$, i.e., $E_r^{p,0} \approx \text{Kernel } d_{r-1}$. Hence

$$E_{r-1}^{p-r,r-1} = \text{Image } d_{r-1} \approx \frac{E_{r-1}^{p,0}}{\text{Kernel } d_{r-1}} \approx \frac{E_{r-1}^{p,0}}{E_r^{p,0}}$$

But by reasoning similar to that of Part 1, $E_{r-1}^{p-r,r-1}$ is finitely generated, and we have assumed that $E_r^{p,0}$ is finitely generated; hence $E_{r-1}^{p,0}$ is finitely generated. Hence by induction $H_p(B) \approx E_2^{p,0}$ is finitely generated. Q.E.D.

REMARK 3.7.4. *The result holds if we replace homology with integer coefficients by homology with coefficients in a field.*

THEOREM 3.7.5. *Suppose that G is Z or a field and that the base of a fibre space X of fibre F is a G-homology n-sphere (i.e., $H_0(B;G) \approx H_n(B;G) \approx G$, $H_i(B;G) = 0$ otherwise), $n > 1$. Then there is an exact sequence*

$$\cdots \to H_q(F) \xrightarrow{i_*} H_q(X) \to H_{q-n}(F) \xrightarrow{d_n} H_{q-1}(F) \to \cdots$$

PROOF. We have $E_2^{p,q} = H_p(B;H_q(F;G)) = 0$ if $0 \neq p \neq n$, $E_2^{0,q} \approx E_2^{n,q} \approx H_q(F;G)$. Hence for $r > 1$, d_r is trivial except when $r = n$, so that $E_2 = E_n$ and $E_{n+1} = E_\infty$. Therefore

$$E_\infty^{n,q} = E_{n+1}^{n,q} \approx \frac{\text{Kernel } d_n}{\text{Image } d_n} = \frac{\text{Kernel } d_n}{d_n(E_n^{2n,q-n+1})} \approx \text{Kernel } d_n$$

$$E_\infty^{0,q} = E_{n+1}^{0,q} \approx \frac{\text{Kernel } d_n}{\text{Image } d_n} = \frac{E_n^{0,q}}{d_n(E_n^{n,q-n+1})}$$

Consider the diagram

$$\begin{array}{ccccc}
E_\infty^{0,q} & \xrightarrow{f_2} & H_q(X) & \xrightarrow{f_3} & E_\infty^{n,q-n} \\
\uparrow f_1 & \nearrow i & & \searrow f & \downarrow f_4 \\
E_n^{0,q} \approx H_q(F) & & & & H_{q-n}(F) \approx E_n^{n,q-n}
\end{array}$$

where all the mappings are induced by inclusions, so that the diagram is commutative. We have just shown that f_1 is onto; furthermore, $E_\infty^{0,q} = D^{0,q}/D^{-1,q+1} = D^{0,q} \subset H_q(X)$, so that f_2 is an isomorphism into. It follows that Kernel $i_* =$ Kernel $f_2 \circ f_1 =$ Kernel $f_1 =$ Image d_n so that we have exactness at $H(F)$.

Next, we proved above that f_4 is an isomorphism into. Hence Kernel $f_5 =$ Kernel $f_4 \circ f_3 =$ Kernel f_3. Furthermore, since f_1 is onto, we have

$$\text{Image } i_* = \text{Image } f_2 \circ f_1 = \text{Image } f_2 = D^{0,q} = D^{n-1,q-n+1}$$
$$(\text{since } E_\infty^{p,q-p} = 0 \text{ for } 0 \neq p \neq n)$$

But $H_q(X) = D^{q,0} = D^{n,q-n}$; so, since

$$E_\infty^{n,q-n} = \frac{D^{n,q-n}}{D^{n-1,q-n+1}}$$

it follows that Kernel f_5 = Kernel $f_3 = D^{n-1,q-n+1}$ = Image i_*, so that we have exactness at $H_q(X)$.

Finally, we note that since $D^{n,q-n} = H_q(X)$, f_3 is onto, so that Image f_5 = Image $f_4 \circ f_3$ = Image f_4 = Kernel d_n, and our proof is complete.

Theorem 3.7.5 is due to H. C. Wang [24], who did not use spectral sequences. However, he assumed some regularity conditions, including the assumption that B is actually an n-sphere. We give a similar proof here.

Let $B = S^n = \{(t_0,\cdots,t_n) \in R^{n+1} | \sum_{i=0}^{n} t_i^2 = 1\}$

$$\begin{aligned} E_+^n &= \{(t_0,\cdots,t_n) \in S^n | t_0 \geq 0\} \\ E_-^n &= \{(t_0,\cdots,t_n) \in S^n | t_0 \leq 0\} \\ S^{n-1} &= \{(t_0,\cdots,t_n) \in S^n | t_0 = 0\} \end{aligned}$$

Then $S^n = E_+^n \cup E_-^n$, $S^{n-1} = E_+^n \cap E_-^n$. Furthermore, let

$$\begin{aligned} &U_+ = \pi^{-1}(E_+^n) \\ &U_- = \pi^{-1}(E_-^n) \\ &U_0 = U_+ \cap U_- = \pi^{-1}(S^{n-1}) \\ &b_0 \in S^{n-1},\ \pi^{-1}(b_0) = F \end{aligned}$$

Assume that (U_-,F) is a pair for which the conclusion of Corollary 3.1.7 holds; in particular, it is sufficient that (U_-,F) be a relative CW complex. Then E_- is contractable, relative to b_0, to b_0, say by a retracting deformation $r: E_- \times I \to E_-$ for which

$$\begin{aligned} r(x,0) &= x, & x &\in E_- \\ r(x,1) &= b_0, & x &\in E_- \\ r(b_0,t) &= b_0, & t &\in I \end{aligned}$$

Define a map $f: U_- \times I \to B$ by

$$f(x,t) = r(\pi(x),t)$$

and a map $g: U_- \times 0 \cup F \times I \to X$ by

$$\begin{aligned} g(x,0) &= x & x &\in U_- \\ g(x,t) &= x & x &\in F,\ t \in I \end{aligned}$$

Then the hypotheses of Corollary 3.1.7 certainly hold and the conclusion follows by our assumption. Since $\pi(G(x,1)) = f(x,1) = b_0$, we have that

$$\begin{aligned} G(x,1) &\in \pi^{-1}(b_0) = F & x &\in U_- \\ G(x,t) &= g(x,t) = x & x &\in F \end{aligned}$$

so that G is a deformation by retraction of U_- onto F. It follows that $H_q(U_-,F) = 0$ for all $q \geq 0$, and then, by the exactness of the homology sequence for the triple (X,U_-,F), it follows that $H_q(X,F) \approx H_q(X,U_-)$, $q \geq 0$. But by excision $H_q(X,U_-) \approx H_q(U_+,U_0)$. Hence $H_q(X,F) \approx H_q(U_+,U_0)$.

Before we proceed, let us note that if X is any fibre space over B, P a polyhedron, $f:P \times I^n \to B$, $h:P \to X$ mappings for which $f(p,(0,\cdots,0)) = (\pi \circ h)(p)$ for all $p \in P$, then there is a map $H:P \times I^n \to X$ for which $H(p,(0,\cdots,0)) = h(p)$ for all $p \in P$ and $\pi \circ H = f$. This is a trivial consequence of the definition of fibre space.

Now let us assume that the fibre F in our case is a polyhedron, let $f:E_+ \times F \to E_+$ be given by

$$f(b,y) = b, \qquad b \in E_+,\ y \in F$$

and let $h:F \to U_+$ be given by

$$h(y) = y, \qquad y \in F$$

Since (E_+,b_0) is homeomorphic to $(I^n,(0,\cdots,0))$ and U_+ is a fibre space over E_+, it follows that there exists a map $H_1:E_+ \times F \to U_+$ for which

$$H_1(b_0,y) = h(y) = y, \qquad y \in F$$

and

$$(\pi \circ H_1)(b,y) = f(b,y) = b, \qquad b \in E_+,\ y \in F$$

Furthermore, let $H_2:U_+ \to E_+ \times F$ be given by

$$H_2(x) = (\pi(X),G_+(x,1))$$

where $G_+(x,t)$ is defined in the same way for E_+ that $G(x,t)$ was defined for E_-. Then $H_1 \circ H_2:U_+ \to U_+$. Now since E_+ is a homeomorph of I^n, $\pi(x)$ is homotopic to the constant map of U_+ into b_0. Hence $H_2(x)$ is homotopic to the map $H_2'(x):U_+ \to E_+$ given by

$$H_2'(x) = (b_0,G_+(x,1))$$

Hence $H_1 \circ H_2$ is homotopic to $H_1 \circ H_2'$. But

$$(H_1 \circ H_2')(x) = H_1(b_0,G_+(x,1))$$

and $G_+(x,1) \in F$. Hence

$$(H_1 \circ H_2')(x) = G_+(x,1)$$

Hence $(H_1 \circ H_2)(x)$ is homotopic to $G_+(x,1)$. On the other hand, G_+ itself provides a homotopy between $x = G_+(x,0)$ and $G_+(x,1)$. It follows that $H_1 \circ H_2$ is homotopic to the identity.

Now let us examine $H_2 \circ H_1$. We have

$$\begin{aligned}(H_2 \circ H_1)(b,y) &= ((\pi \circ H_1)(b,y),G_+(H_1(b,y),1))\\ &= (b,G_+(H_1(b,y),1))\end{aligned}$$

Because E_+ is a homeomorph of I^n, this is clearly homotopic to

$$(b,G_+(H_1(b_0,y),1)) = (b,G_+(y,1)) \\ = (b,y)$$

since G_+ is a deformation retraction of U_+ onto F, and $y \in F$. Hence $H_2 \circ H_1$ is also homotopic to the identity. It follows that $E_+ \times F$ and U_+ have the same homotopy type. What is more, H_1 carries $S^{n-1} \times F$ into U_0 and H_2 carries U_0 into $S^{n-1} \times F$, so that the pairs $(E^n_+ \times F, S^{n-1} \times F)$ and (U_+,U_0) also have the same homotopy type. Hence $H_q(U_+,U_0) \approx H_q(E^n_+ \times F, S^{n-1} \times F)$. Now $H_q(E^n_+ \times F, E^{n-1}_- \times F) = 0$ for all q, since both E^n_+ and E^{n-1}_- are contractible. Hence by the exactness of the homology sequence for the triple $(E^n_+ \times F, S^{n-1} \times F, E^{n-1} \times F)$, we have $H_q(E^n_+ \times F, S^{n-1} \times F) \approx H_{q-1}(S^{n-1} \times F, E^{n-1}_- \times F)$. By excision, this, in turn is isomorphic to $H_{q-1}(E^{n-1}_+ \times F, S^{n-2} \times F)$. So

$$H_q(E^n_+ \times F, S^{n-1} \times F) \approx H_{q-1}(E^{n-1}_+ \times F, S^{n-2} \times F)$$

Proceeding in this way, we finally obtain

$$H_q(E^n_+ \times F, S^{n-1} \times F) \approx H_{q-n}(E^0_+ \times F, S^{-1} \times F) \\ \approx H_{q-n}(F,\phi) \\ \approx H_{q-n}(F)$$

[An alternative method for proving this is by the use of the Künneth theorem as follows:

$$H_q((E^n_+,S^{n-1}) \times F) = \sum_{s+t=q} \oplus H_s(E^n_+,S^{n-1}) \otimes H_t(F)$$

The only s for which the first term is not zero is $s = n$. Hence

$$H_q((E^n_+,S^{n-1}) \times F) = H_n(E^n_+,S^{n-1}) \otimes H_{q-n}(F) \\ = Z \otimes H_{q-n}(F) \\ = H_{q-n}(F)$$

(The same holds for any coefficient group.)]

We have proved that $H_q(X,F) \approx H_{q-n}(F)$. The Wang theorem now follows from the exactness of the homology sequence for (X,F).

3.8 Applications to Spheres [8, 19, 25, 27]

Let $B = S^n$, $b_0 \in B$, $X = (B,b_0)^{(I,0)}$ (i.e., the space of paths in X starting at b_0), and define $\pi: X \to B$ by

$$\pi(f) = f(1)$$

We have seen (Section 3.1) that X is a fibre space over B with fibre $F = \pi^{-1}(b_0) =$ the space $F^1(B,b_0)$ of loops in B based at b_0.

LEMMA 3.8.1. *X is contractible*

PROOF. We retract "along the paths"; more precisely, define a map $F: X \times I \to X$ by

$$F(f,t)(s) = f(ts), \qquad t,s \in I, \quad f \in X$$

Then $F(f,0)(s) = f(0s) = f(0) = b_0$, so that $F(f,0)$ is the constant path, and $F(f,1)(s) = f(1s) = f(s)$, so that $F(f,1) = f$.

COROLLARY 3.8.2. $H_{q-n}(F) \approx H_{q-1}(F)$, $q > 1$.

PROOF. This follows at once from 3.8.1 and 3.7.5.

COROLLARY 3.8.3.

$$H_{k(n-1)}(F) \approx Z, \qquad k \geq 0$$
$$H_q(F) = 0, \qquad q \neq k(n-1)$$

PROOF. From Corollary 3.8.2 it follows that $H_{q-(n-1)}(F) \approx H_q(F)$. Hence

$$\begin{aligned} H_{k(n-1)}(F) &= H_{(n-1)+(k-1)(n-1)}(F) \\ &\approx H_{(k-1)(n-1)}(F) \approx \cdots \approx H_0(F) \approx Z \end{aligned}$$

The other half follows in a similar manner.

DEFINITION. *A path in* E^n_+ *or in* E^n_- *is a* straight *path if and only if its perpendicular projection into the plane* $y_0 = 0$ *is straight.*

Let $y \in S^{n-1}$. We may then define paths $f_-(y)$ and $f_+(y)$ in E^n_- and E^n_+, respectively, by the condition that they shall be the unique straight paths from b_0 to y in E^n_- and E^n_+, respectively. We can now define a mapping $\phi: S^{n-1} \to F$ by

$$\phi(y) = f_-(y) \cdot \widehat{f_+(y)}, \qquad y \in S^{n-1}$$

Then ϕ is continuous and one-one, and since S^{n-1} is compact, ϕ^{-1} is also continuous. Hence S^{n-1} is homeomorphic to a subset of F. Now since X is contractible, we deduce from Corollary 3.2.4 that $\pi_{i-1}(F) \approx \pi_i(B) = \pi_i(S^n)$. Hence ϕ induces homomorphisms

$$\phi_*: \pi_{i-1}(S^{n-1}) \to \pi_{i-1}(F) \approx \pi_i(S^n)$$

The composition $E: \pi_{i-1}(S^{n-1}) \to \pi_i(S^n)$ is called the *suspension*.

To see the significance of the suspension, consider the diagram

$$\begin{array}{ccc} \pi_{i-1}(S^{n-1}) & \xrightarrow{E} & \pi_i(S^n) \\ \uparrow{\scriptstyle \partial_*} & & \downarrow{\scriptstyle j_*} \\ \pi_i(E^n_-, S^{n-1}) & \xrightarrow{\theta_*} & \pi_i(S^n, E^n_+) \end{array} \qquad (*)$$

Both j_* and ∂_* are isomorphisms onto, since E^n_+ and E^n_- are both contractable; θ_* is the excision homomorphism. Hence the suspension E in a sense measures the extent to which the excision homomorphism fails to be an isomorphism onto.

LEMMA 3.8.4. *For $i = n$, E is an isomorphism onto.*

PROOF. Let $n > 1$. Since $\rho:\pi_{n-1}(S^{n-1}) \approx H_{n-1}(S^{n-1})$, it follows from the commutativity of the diagram

$$\begin{array}{ccccccc} 0 = H_n(E^n_-) & \longrightarrow & H_n(E^n_-,S^{n-1}) & \xrightarrow{\partial_*} & H_{n-1}(S^{n-1}) & = & H_n(E^n_-) = 0 \\ & & \downarrow \rho' & & \downarrow \rho & & \\ 0 = \pi_n(E^n_-) & \longrightarrow & \pi_n(E^n_-,S^{n-1}) & \xrightarrow{\partial_*} & \pi_{n-1}(S^{n-1}) & \longrightarrow & \pi_{n-1}(E^n_-) = 0 \end{array}$$

that $\rho':H_n(E^n_-,S^{n-1}) \rightarrow \pi_n(E^n_-,S^{n-1})$ is an isomorphism onto. But

$$\rho:H_n(S^n,E^n_+) \rightarrow \pi_n(S^n,E^n_+)$$

is clearly also an isomorphism onto. Hence by the commutativity of the diagram

$$\begin{array}{ccc} H_n(E^n_-,S^{n-1}) & \xrightarrow{\theta_*} & H_n(S^n,E^n_+) \\ \downarrow \rho' & & \downarrow \rho \\ \pi_n(E^n_-,S^{n-1}) & \xrightarrow{\theta_*} & \pi_n(S^n,E^n_+) \end{array}$$

it follows that $\theta_*:\pi_n(E^n_-,S^{n-1}) \rightarrow \pi_n(S^n,E^n_+)$ is an isomorphism onto. The result now follows from (*).

COROLLARY 3.8.5. *$\phi_*:\pi_{n-1}(S^{n-1}) \rightarrow \pi_{n-1}(F)$ is an isomorphism onto.*

COROLLARY 3.8.6. *$\phi_*:H_{n-1}(S^{n-1}) \rightarrow H_{n-1}(F)$ is an isomorphism onto.*

PROOF. We have $H_i(S^{n-1}) = H_i(F) = \pi_i(S^{n-1}) = \pi_i(F) = 0$ for $i < n - 1$; this follows from Corollaries 3.8.3 and 3.8.4. Furthermore, by Corollary 3.8.5 $\phi_*:\pi_{n-1}(S^{n-1}) \rightarrow \pi_{n-1}(F)$ is an isomorphism onto, and hence Theorem 2.10.3 yields that $\phi_*:H_{n-1}(S^{n-1}) \rightarrow H_{n-1}(F)$ is onto. But $H_{n-1}(S^{n-1}) = Z$ and $H_{n-1}(F) = Z$ has no proper finite subgroups. Hence either Kernel $\phi_* = 0$ or Kernel $\phi_* =$ the whole group. The second is impossible because then Image $\phi_* = 0$, contradicting what we just proved. Hence Kernel $\phi_*= 0$. Q.E.D.

Since ϕ is a homeomorphism onto, we may consider S^{n-1} to be a subset of F. We then obtain the following Theorem.

THEOREM 3.8.7. *We have*

$$H_q(F,S^{n-1}) = \begin{cases} 0 & 0 \le q < 2n-2 \\ Z & q = k(n-1) \quad k \ge 2 \\ 0 & otherwise \end{cases}$$

PROOF. Let $n > 1$. Consider the diagram

$$0 = H_n(F) \to H_n(F,S^{n-1}) \xrightarrow{\partial_*} H_{n-1}(S^{n-1}) \xrightarrow{\phi_*}$$
$$H_{n-1}(F) \xrightarrow{j_*} H_{n-1}(F,S^{n-1}) \to H_{n-2}(S^{n-1}) = 0$$

By Corollary 3.8.6, ϕ_* is an isomorphism onto. Hence Image $\partial_* =$ Kernel $\phi_* = 0$. But ∂_* is an isomorphism into. Hence $H_n(F,S^{n-1}) = 0$. Similarly, Kernel $j_* =$ Image $\phi_* =$ the whole group. Hence Image $j_* = 0$. But j_* is onto. Hence $H_{n-1}(F,S^{n-1}) = 0$.

Next, let $q = k(n-1)$, $k \ge 2$. Then $q - 1 > n - 1$, and hence we have the exact sequence

$$0 = H_q(S^{n-1}) \to H_q(F) \to H_q(F,S^{n-1}) \to H_{q-1}(S^{n-1}) = 0$$

Hence $H_q(F,S^{n-1}) \approx H_q(F) \approx z$, by Corollary 3.8.3. Finally, if $q \not\equiv 0 \bmod n-1$, then $H_q(S^{n-1}) = H_{q-1}(S^{n-1}) = 0$, and our result follows as before.

THEOREM 3.8.8. *If $n > 2$, then*

$$E: \pi_{i-1}(S^{n-1}) \approx \pi_i(S^n) \qquad i < 2n-2$$
$$E: \pi_{2n-3}(S^{n-1}) \twoheadrightarrow \pi_{2n-2}(S^n)$$

PROOF. Since $n > 1$, S^n is 1-connected. Hence $\pi_1(S^{n-1})$ acts trivially on $\pi_q(F,S^{n-1})$ for all q, and it then follows from the Hurewicz theorem and Theorem 3.8.7 that

$$\pi_i(F,S^{n-1}) = 0 \qquad i < 2n-2$$
$$\pi_{2n-2}(F,S^{n-1}) = Z$$

Hence from the exact sequence for (F,S^{n-1}), it follows that

$$\phi_*: \pi_i(S^{n-1}) \approx \pi_i(F) \qquad i < 2n-2$$
$$\phi_*: \pi_{2n-3}(S^{n-1}) \twoheadrightarrow \pi_{2n-3}(F)$$

The result now follows at once.

The theorem may be restated in the following slightly more convenient form.

THEOREM 3.8.9. *If $n > 1$, then*

$$E: \pi_i(S^n) \approx \pi_{i+1}(S^{n+1}) \qquad i < 2n-1$$
$$E: \pi_{2n-1}(S^n) \twoheadrightarrow \pi_{2n}(S^{n+1})$$

This theorem was first proved by Freudenthal [8] in 1937, and by highly geometric methods. The previous proof was given by the author in [25].

THEOREM 3.8.10. *If* $n = 2, 4,$ *or* 8, *then*

$$\pi_i(S^n) \approx \pi_{i-1}(S^{n-1}) \oplus \pi_i(S^{2n-1})$$

More precisely, there is a map $h: S^{2n-1} \to S^n$ *such that the two maps*

$$h_*: \pi_i(S^{2n-1}) \to \pi_i(S^n)$$
$$E: \pi_{i-1}(S^{n-1}) \to \pi_i(S^n)$$

induce an isomorphism of $\pi_{i-1}(S^{n-1}) \oplus \pi_i(S^{2n-1})$ *onto* $\pi_i(S^n)$. *In particular, E is always an isomorphism into.*

PROOF. By Section 3.1, there exist fibre maps $h: S^{2n-1} \to S^n$ with S^{n-1} as fibre, for $n = 2, 4,$ and 8. Consider the diagram

$$\begin{array}{ccccccccc} & & & \xrightarrow{j_*} & \pi_i(S^{2n-1}, S^{n-1}) & \xrightarrow{\partial_*} & & & \\ \cdots \to \pi_i(S^{n-1}) & \xrightarrow{i_*} & \pi_i(S^{2n-1}) & \xrightarrow{h_*} & \pi_i(S^n) & \xrightarrow{d_*} & \pi_{i-1}(S^{n-1}) & \to & \pi_{i-1}(S^{2n-1}) \to \cdots \end{array}$$

Since S^{n-1} is a proper subset of S^{2n-1}, S^{n-1} is contractible to a point in S^{2n-1}, and therefore i_* is always trivial. Let $k: (E^n, S^{n-1}) \to (S^{2n-1}, S^{n-1})$ be a map such that $k|S^{n-1} =$ identity (where E^n is an n-cell bounded by S^{n-1}). Define

$$\psi: \pi_{i-1}(S^{n-1}) \to \pi_i(S^{2n-1}, S^{n-1})$$

by

$$\psi = k_* \circ \partial_{1*}^{-1}$$

where $\partial_{1*}: \pi_i(E^n, S^{n-1}) \to \pi_{i-1}(S^{n-1})$ is the boundary mapping. (∂_{1*} is an isomorphism onto because E^n is contractible.)

But since $k|S^{n-1} =$ identity, it follows that $\partial_* \circ k_* = \partial_{1*}$. Hence $\partial_* \circ \psi = \partial_* \circ k_* \circ \partial_{1*}^{-1} = \partial_{1*} \circ \partial_{1*}^{-1} =$ identity. Hence

$$\pi_i(S^{2n-1}, S^{n-1}) = \text{Image } \psi \oplus \text{Kernel } \partial_*$$

Now ψ is an isomorphism into, while ∂_* is onto. Since i_* is trivial, j_* is an isomorphism of $\pi_i(S^{2n-1})$ onto Image $j_* =$ Kernel ∂_*. Hence

$$\psi: \pi_{i-1}(S^{n-1}) \to \pi_i(S^{2n-1}, S^{n-1})$$

and

$$j_*: \pi_i(S^{2n-1}) \to \pi_i(S^{2n-1}, S^{n-1})$$

induce an isomorphism of

$$\pi_i(S^{n-1}) \oplus \pi_i(S^{2n-1}) \text{ onto } \pi_i(S^{2n-1}, S^{n-1})$$

Hence if we let h_{1*} be the map of Theorem 3.2.1, it follows that $h_{1*} \circ \psi$ and $h_{1*} \circ j_*$ induce an isomorphism

$$\pi_{i-1}(S^{n-1}) \oplus \pi_1(S^{2n-1}) \approx \pi_i(S^n)$$

Now a glance at the diagram

$$\begin{array}{ccccccccc}
 & & & \pi_i(S^{2n-1},S^{n-1}) & & & & & \\
 & & \nearrow^{j_*} & \downarrow{\scriptstyle h_{1*}} & \nwarrow^{\psi} & \searrow^{\partial *} & & & \\
\cdots \to \pi_i(S^{n-1}) & \xrightarrow{i_*} & \pi_i(S^{2n-1}) & \xrightarrow{h_*} \pi_i(S^n) & \xrightarrow{d_*} & \pi_{i-1}(S^{n-1}) & \to & \pi_{i-1}(S^{2n-1}) & \to \cdots
\end{array}$$

will reveal that $h_* = h_{1*} \circ j_*$. The proof that $h_{1*} \circ \psi = \pm E$ will be left to the reader.

COROLLARY 3.8.11.

$$h_*: \pi_i(S^3) \approx \pi_i(S^2), \qquad i > 2$$

In particular, $\pi_3(S^2)$ is the infinite cyclic group of which the homotopy class of h is a generator.

3.9 Certain Fibrations [19]

Let X be a topological space, $E = (X,x)^{(I,0)}$, $\tilde{X}$ the universal covering space of X, and $E = (\tilde{X},\tilde{x})^{(I,0)}$. Let F_0 be the path component of $F^1(X,x)$ which contains e_x. Then the covering mapping from $\tilde{X}$ onto X induces a homeomorphism from $\tilde{E}$ onto E which sends $F^1(\tilde{X},\tilde{x})$ homeomorphically onto F_0.

We now define two sequences $\{X_i\}$ and $\{\tilde{X}_i\}$ in the following way:

$$X_0 = X, \qquad \tilde{X}_0 = \tilde{X}$$
$$X_{i+1} = F^1(\tilde{X}_i,\tilde{x}_i) \qquad \tilde{X}_i = \text{the universal covering space of } X_i$$

Then X_{i+1} is the fibre for a fibre map $Y_{i+1} \to \tilde{X}_i$, where Y_{i+1} is contractable; indeed we have $Y_{i+1} = (\tilde{X}_i,x_i)^{(I,0)}$.

THEOREM 3.9.1. *Let X be a connected $lc^{1/2}$ space, $\pi: \tilde{X} \to X$ the covering mapping. Then $\tilde{X}$ is 1-connected and*

$$\pi_*: \pi_i(\tilde{X}) \approx \pi_i(X) \qquad i > 1$$

THEOREM 3.9.2. *Let X be an $(n-1)$-connected space, $n \geq 1$. Then there is a fibre map $\pi: Y \to X$ such that*

1. *Y is n-connected.*
2. $\pi_*: \pi_i(Y) \approx \pi_i(X) \qquad i > n$

PROOF. By Theorem 2.10.1 with $R = 0$, there is a relative CW complex (X^*,X) such that

$$i_*:\pi_i(X) \approx \pi_i(X^*) \qquad i \leq n$$
$$\pi_i(X^*) = 0 \qquad i > n$$

Let $Y = E_{x,X}(X^*)$, $Y^* = E_{x,X^*}(X^*)$, where $E_{x,A}(X^*)$ is the space of paths in X^* beginning at x and ending in the subspace A of X^*.

Consider the diagram

$$\begin{array}{ccccccccc}
\longrightarrow \pi_{i+1}(Y^*) & \xrightarrow{j_*} & \pi_{i+1}(Y^*,Y) & \xrightarrow{\partial_*} & \pi_i(Y) & \xrightarrow{i_*} & \pi_i(Y^*) & \longrightarrow & \pi_i(Y^*,Y) \\
\downarrow & & \downarrow & & & & \downarrow & & \downarrow \\
\longrightarrow \pi_{i+1}(X^*) & \xrightarrow{j'_*} & \pi_{i+1}(X^*,X) & \xrightarrow{\partial'} & \pi_i(X) & \xrightarrow{i'_*} & \pi_i(X^*) & \longrightarrow & \pi_i(X^*,X)
\end{array}$$

the vertical homomorphism from $\pi_{i+1}(Y^*,Y)$ to $\pi_{i+1}(X^*,X)$ being an isomorphism onto. If $i > n$, then $\pi_i(X^*) = \pi_{i+1}(X^*) = 0$, while if $i < n - 1$, then the same equation follows from $\pi_i(X^*) \approx \pi_i(X)$, which is zero because X is $(n - 1)$-connected. Hence for $i \neq n$, $n - 1$, ∂'_* is an isomorphism onto. But Y^* is contractible, and hence ∂_* is always an isomorphism onto. Hence for $i \neq n$, $n - 1$, π_* is an isomorphism onto; in particular, $\pi_i(Y) = 0$ for $i < n - 1$.

Next, let $i = n$. Since $\pi_{n+1}(X^*) = 0$, ∂'_* is an isomorphism into. But i'_* is an isomorphism onto, and hence Image ∂'_* = Kernel $i'_* = 0$.Hence $\pi_{n+1}(X^*,X) = 0$. Hence $\pi_{n+1}(Y^*,Y) = 0$, and it follows that $\pi_n(Y) = 0$.

Finally, let $i = n - 1$. Since $\pi_n(X)$ is mapped isomorphically onto $\pi_n(X^*)$, it follows that Kernel j'_* = the whole group, so that Image $i'_* = 0$. Hence ∂'_* is an isomorphism into. But $\pi_{n-1}(X) = 0$. Hence $\pi_n(X^*,X) = 0$, and it follows as before that $\pi_{n-1}(Y) = 0$. The proof is complete.

COROLLARY 3.9.3. *Let F be the space of loops in X^*. Then*

$$\pi_i(F) = 0 \qquad i < n - 1$$
$$\pi_{n-1}(F) = \pi_n(X)$$

In short, F is an Eilenberg-MacLane space of type $[\pi_n(X),n - 1]$.

PROOF. This is an immediate consequence of the fact that $\pi_i(F) \approx \pi_{i+1}(X^*)$, which in turn follows from the fact that Y^* is contractible and that F is the fibre of the fibre mapping of Y^* onto X^*.

COROLLARY 3.9.4. *There is a fibre map $\pi':X' \to X^*$, such that X' has the same homotopy type as X, and whose fibre is Y.*

PROOF. Take X' to be the space of all paths in X^* that end in X, $\pi'(f) = f(0)$.

3.10 The Spectral Sequence for Cohomology [19]

Let $\pi: X \to B$ be a fibre map, F the fibre. Let G' be a commutative ring with identity, $C^*(X,G) = \text{Hom}\,\{C(X),G\}$. If $B \subset C(X)$, then the *annihilator* of B is $\{f \in C^*(X,G) | f(B) = 0\}$, and is denoted by Ann (B). Let

$$A^{*p} = \text{Ann}\,(A^{p-1})$$
$$A^{*p,q} = C^{p+q}(X;G) \cap A^{*p}$$

From the facts $A^{-1} = 0$, $A^{p-1} \subset A^p$, and $\partial A^p \subset A^p$, it follows that $A^{*0} = C^*(X,G)$, $A^{*p} \supset A^{*p+1}$, and $\delta A^{*p} \subset A^{*p}$.

Define

$$C_r^{*p,q} = A^{*p,q} \cap \delta^{-1}(A^{*p+r,q-r+1})$$
$$D_r^{*p,q} = A^{*p,q} \cap \delta A^{*p-r,q+r-1}$$
$$E_r^{*p,q} = C_r^{*p,q}/C_{r-1}^{*p+1,q-1} + D_{r-1}^{*p,q}$$

analogously to the definition of the spectral sequence in the case of homology. Then

$$E_r^* = \sum_{p,q} E_r^{*p,q}$$

is a complex with a boundary operator

$$d_r: E_r^{*p,q} \to E_r^{*p+r,q-r+1}$$

Note that $A^{*p} \cup A^{*q} \subset A^{*p+q}$, where $\cup$ denotes the usual cup product. The cup product in $C^*(X;G)$ induces a multiplication in E_r^*, and we have

$$E_r^{*p,q} \cdot E_r^{*s,t} \subset E_r^{*p+s,q+t}$$

As in the case of homology, we have that $E_2^{*p,q} = H^p(B;H^q(F;G))$ if $\pi_1(B)$ operates trivially on $H^*(F;G)$. The product that is induced in E_2^* by the cup product in $C^*(X;G)$ agrees up to a sign with the cup product in $H^p(B)$ with the coefficients multiplying like the cup product in $H^q(F)$. In fact, if we denote by ρ the isomorphism from $E_2^{*p,q}$ to $H^p(B;H^q(F;G))$, then for $u \in E_2^{*p,q}$, $v \in E_2^{*r,s}$, we have that $\rho(u\cdot v) = (-1)^{qr}\rho(u) \cup \rho(v)$. Furthermore, for the multiplication defined above in E_r^* (denoted by a dot), we obtain

$$d_r(u\cdot v) = d_r(u)\cdot v + (-1)^{p+q}u\cdot d_r(v)$$

where $u \in E_r^{*p,q}$, $v \in {}_r^{*s,t}$.

THEOREM 3.10.1. *Let G be Z or a field, and suppose that B is a G-cohomology n-sphere. Then there is an exact sequence*

$$\cdots \to H^q(X) \xrightarrow{i_*} H^q(F) \xrightarrow{\theta} H^{q-n+1}(F) \to H^{q+1}(X) \to \cdots$$

where $\theta: H^*(F) \to H^*(F)$ *is a derivation of degree* $n - 1$;
i.e.,

$$\theta(u \cdot v) = \theta(u) \cdot v + (-1)^{pn} u \cdot \theta(v)$$

for

$$u \in H^p(F), \qquad v \in H^q(F)$$

PROOF. By the universal coefficient theorem, we have that $H^p(B;\Gamma) \approx H^p(B,G) \otimes \Gamma$ if either $G = Z$ and $H^p(B,Z)$ is finitely generated and free for each p, or G is a field F and Γ is a vector space over F and $H^p(B;F)$ is finitely generated for all p. Since B is a G-cohomology n-sphere, one or the other of these conditions is always satisfied for $\Gamma = H^q(F;G)$. Hence we have that

$$E_2^{*p,q} = H^p(B;H^q(F;G)) = H^p(B;G) \otimes H^q(F;G)$$

Hence

$$E_2^{*p,q} \approx \begin{cases} H^0(B) \otimes H^q(F) \approx H^q(F) & p = 0 \\ 0 \otimes H^q(F) \approx 0 & p \neq 0,n \\ H^n(B) \otimes H^q(F) \approx H^q(F) & p = n \end{cases}$$

Next, note that d_r is trivial unless $r = n$, so that we have

$$E_2^* = \cdots = E_n^*, \qquad E_{n+1}^* = \cdots = E_\infty^*$$

Let α and β denote the isomorphisms from $E_n^{*0,q}$ to $H^q(F)$ and from $E_n^{*n,q-n+1}$ to $H^{q-n+1}(F)$, respectively. Consider then the diagram

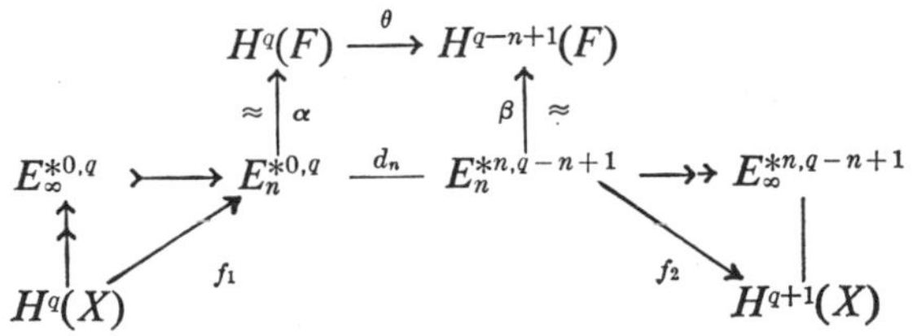

where the mappings f_1, f_2, and θ are defined by demanding that the diagram be commutative and the other unnamed mappings are defined in a manner analogous to the proof of Theorem 3.7.5. The exactness of the sequence in Theorem 3.10.1 then follows in a manner analogous to that of Theorem 3.7.5. It remains to prove that θ is a derivation of degree $n - 1$.

To this end, suppose we let α and β be given by $\alpha(1 \otimes y) = y$ and $\beta(s \otimes y) = y$, respectively, where s is a generator of $H^n(B)$. Now $\theta \circ \alpha = \beta \circ d_n$. Hence we obtain

$$\begin{aligned} \theta(xy) &= \theta(\alpha(1 \otimes xy)) = (\theta \circ \alpha)(1 \otimes xy) \\ &= (\beta \circ d_n)(1 \otimes xy) = \beta(d_n(1 \otimes x) \cdot (1 \otimes y)) \\ &= \beta((d_n(1 \otimes x))(1 \otimes y) + (1 \otimes x) d_n(1 \otimes y)) \end{aligned}$$

$$= \beta((\beta^{-1}(\beta \circ d_n)(1 \otimes x))(1 \otimes y) + (1 \otimes x)\beta^{-1}(\beta \circ d_n)(1 \otimes y))$$
$$= \beta((\beta^{-1}\theta(x))(1 \otimes y) + (1 \otimes x)\beta^{-1}\theta(y))$$

Now $\beta^{-1}(z) = s \otimes z$; hence we obtain

$$\theta(xy) = \beta((s \otimes \theta(x))(1 \otimes y) + (1 \otimes x)(s \otimes \theta(y)))$$

If we apply to this the formula

$$(a \otimes b)(c \otimes d) = (-1)^{qr}(ac) \otimes (bd)$$

for

$$b \in H^q(F), \qquad d \in H^r(b)$$

then we obtain

$$\begin{aligned} \theta(xy) &= \beta(s \otimes [\theta(x)\cdot y] + (-1)^{pn}s \otimes [x\cdot\theta(y)]) \\ &= \beta(s \otimes (\theta(x)\cdot y) + (-1)^{pn}x\cdot\theta(y)) \\ &= \theta(x)\cdot y + (-1)^{pn}x\cdot\theta(y) \end{aligned}$$

Q.E.D.

THEOREM 3.10.2. *If $G = Z$ or a field and F is a G-cohomology n-sphere, then there is an exact sequence*

$$\cdots \to H^p(B) \xrightarrow{\pi^*} H^p(X) \to H^{p-n}(B) \xrightarrow{\phi} H^{p+1}(B) \to \cdots$$

and an $\omega \in H^{n+1}(B)$ such that
1. $\phi(x) = \omega x \qquad x \in H^{p-n}(B)$.
2. $2\omega = 0 \qquad n$ *even.*

The following applications of the foregoing theorems are listed without proof.

THEOREM 3.10.3. *Denote by $K(\Pi,n)$ an Eilenberg-MacLane space of type (Π,n), by $H^*(\Pi,n;G)$ its cohomology ring with coefficients in G. Let R_0 denote the additive group of rationals. Then we have that for n even,*

$$H^*(Z,n;R_0) = R_0[\mu] = \text{polynomial ring in } \mu, \text{ where } n = \dim \mu$$

and for n odd,

$$H^*(Z,n;R_0) = \wedge[\mu] = \text{Grassman algebra in } \mu$$

where $n = \dim \mu$.

It follows that for n even

$$H^q(Z,n;R_0) = \begin{cases} 0, & q \not\equiv 0 \pmod{n} \\ R_0(\mu^k) & q = kn \end{cases}$$

and for n odd, $K(Z,n)$ is an R_0-cohomology n-sphere.

THEOREM 3.10.4. *Let $\pi: X \to B$ with fibre F, and suppose that G is Z or a field. Then*

1. $\pi^*: H^*(B) \approx H^*(X)$ *if and only if F is acyclic.*
2. $i^*: H^*(X) \approx H^*(F)$ *if and only if B is acyclic.*

COROLLARY 3.10.5. $H^*(Z_n,n;Z_p)$ *is trivial if* $(m,p) = 1$.

THEOREM 3.10.6. $\pi_i(S^n)$ *is finite if $i > n$ and n is odd.*

THEOREM 3.10.7. $K(\Pi,n)$ *is R_0-acyclic if Π is finite.*

References

Journals

1. A. L. Blakers, *Some relations between homology and homotopy groups*, Ann. of Math. **49** (1948), 428–461.
2. S. Eilenberg, *On the relation between the fundamental group of a space and the higher homotopy groups*, Fund. Math. **32** (1939), 167–175.
3. S. Eilenberg, *Cohomology and continuous mappings*, Ann. of Math. **41** (1940), 231–251.
4. S. Eilenberg, *Singular homology theory*, Ann. of Math. **45** (1944), 407–447.
5. S. Eilenberg and S. MacLane, *Relations between homology and homotopy groups of spaces*, Ann. of Math. **46** (1945), 480–509.
6. S. Eilenberg and S. MacLane, *Acyclic models*, Amer. J. Math. **75** (1953), 189–199.
7. R. H. Fox, *On topologies for function spaces*, Bull. Amer. Math. Soc. **51** (1945), 429–432.
8. H. Freudenthal, *Über die Klassen der Sphärenabbildungen*, Compositio Math. **5** (1937), 299–314; also *Note on the homotopy groups of spheres*, Quart. J. Math. Oxford **20** (1949), 62–64.
9. W. Gysin, *Zur Homologietheorie der Abbildungen und Faserungen der Mannigfaltigkeiten*, Comment. Math. Helv. **14** (1941), 61–122.
10. H. Hopf, *Die Klassen der Abbildungen der n-dimensionalen Polyeder auf die n-dimensionalen Sphäre*, Comment. Math. Helv. **5** (1933), 39–54.
11. H. Hopf, *Über die Abbildungen von sphären auf sphären niedrigerer dimension*, Fund. Math. **25** (1935), 427–440.
12. S.-T. Hu, *An exposition of the relative homotopy theory*, Duke Math. J. **14** (1947), 991–1033.
13. S.-T. Hu, *The homotopy addition theorem*, Ann. of Math. **58** (1953), 108–122.
14. W. Hurewicz, *Beiträge zur Topologie der Deformationen*, Verh. Nederl. Akad. Wetensch. **38** (1935), 112–119, 521–528; **39** (1936), 117–126, 215–224.

15. W. Hurewicz and N. E. Steenrod, *Homotopy relations in fibre spaces*, Proc. Nat. Acad. Sci. U.S.A. **27** (1941) 60–64.
16. J. R. Jackson, *Spaces of mappings on topological products with applications to homotopy theory*, Proc. Amer. Math. Soc. **3** (1952), 327–333.
17. J. Leray, *L'anneau spectral et l'anneau filtré d'homologie d'un espace localement compact et d'une application continué*, J. Math. Pures App. **29** (1950), 1–139.
18. J. C. Moore, *Some applications of homology theory to homotopy problems*, Ann. of Math. **58** (1953), 325–350.
19. J.-P. Serre, *Homologie singulière des espaces fibrés*, Ann. of Math. **54** (1951), 425–505.
20. J.-P. Serre, *Groupes d'homotopie et classes de groupes abéliens*, Ann. of Math. **58** (1953), 258–294.
21. N. E. Steenrod, *Homology with local coefficients*, Ann. of Math. **44** (1943), 610–627.
22. N. E. Steenrod, *Products of cocycles and extensions of mappings*, Ann. of Math. **48** (1947), 290–320.
23. H. C. Wang, *Some examples concerning the relations between homology and homotopy groups*, Verh. Nederl. Akad. Wetensch. **50** (1947), 384–386.
24. H. C. Wang, *The homology groups of the fibre bundles over a sphere*, Duke Math. J. **16** (1949), 33–38.
25. G. W. Whitehead, *On the Freudenthal theorems*, Ann. of Math. **57** (1953), 209–228.
26. J. H. C. Whitehead, *Combinatorial homotopy I*, Bull. Amer. Math. Soc. **55** (1949), 213–245.
27. J. H. C. Whitehead, *Note on suspension*, Quart. J. Math. Oxford **1** (1950), 9–22.
28. J. H. C. Whitehead, *On the theory of obstructions*, Ann. of Math. **54** (1951), 68–83.
29. H. Whitney, *On maps of an n-sphere into another n-sphere*, Duke Math. J. **3** (1937), 46–50.
30. H. Whitney, *The maps of an n-complex into an n-sphere*, Duke Math. J. **3** (1937), 51–55.

Books

B.1. W. Hurewicz and H. Wallman, *Dimension theory*, Princeton University Press, Princeton, New Jersey, 1941.
B.2. S. Lefschetz, *Algebraic topology*, American Mathematical Society, Providence, Rhode Island, 1942.
B.3. S. Eilenberg and N. Steenrod, *Foundations of algebraic topology*, Princeton University Press, Princeton, New Jersey, 1952.
B.4. H. Seifert and W. Threlfall, *Lehrbuch der Topologie*, Chelsea Publishing Company, New York, 1963.
B.5. N. Steenrod, *Topology of fibre bundles*, Princeton University Press, Princeton, New Jersey, 1951.

[redacted]

[redacted]